LOOK at the SKY

....and tell the Weather

FOREWORD TO THE REVISED EDITION

In most part, this book is a reprint. A writer is seldom completely satisfied with his works but there is always one book which gives him the most satisfaction; in my case this was LOOK AT THE SKY. Written many years ago, it dragged along without advertising or even an announcement by the publisher on publication day. When that firm sold out, the book became an even sadder stepchild on my list of writings. I used to wake up in the middle of the night, scheming how to buy the book back for republication, wondering how much money I would need to tempt the publisher. My royalty check at this point was for ten dollars and ninety cents.

If you don't believe in the power of prayer, you'd better begin, for then came a letter from the publisher announcing they were remaindering my book and the complete rights were mine for the asking! For a book to be remaindered is a kiss of death to an author; it usually shakes his confidence, but to me it was a prayer answered.

So here is my favorite Sloane book with a few new things added. I hope that you find in it that spark which insisted on and resulted in an encore and that it enriches your life each time you look at the sky.

ERIC SLOANE
Cornwall Bridge,
Connecticut

Revised and enlarged edition

LOOK at the SKY ...and tell the weather

by ERIC SLOANE

HAWTHORN BOOKS, INC.
Publishers/NEW YORK
A Howard & Wyndham Company

Praised be the Lord
For our Brother the Wind
And for Air and Cloud,
Calms and all Weather.
        ST. FRANCIS OF ASSISI

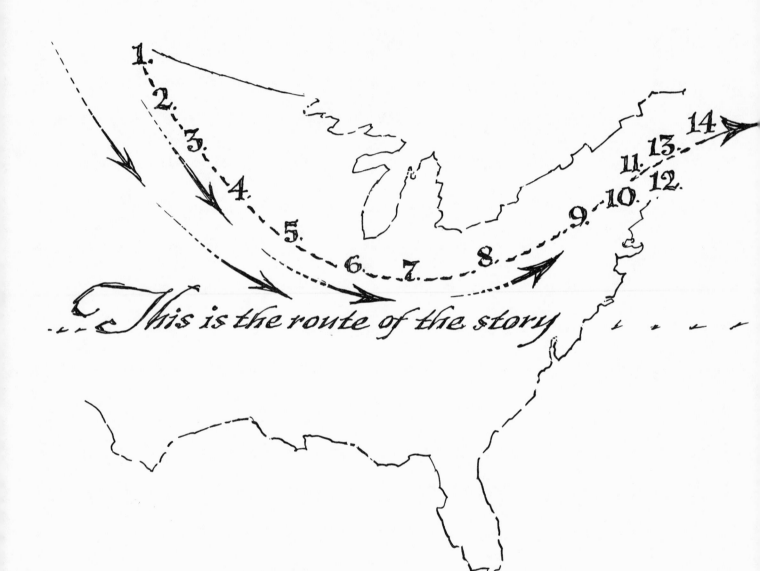

This is the route of the story

Contents:

Author's Note

CENTURIES AGO Cato the Censor is reported to have said, "I wonder how one haruspex [weatherman] can look another in the face without laughing." Since that time the weatherman has developed a lessened sense of humor. I can see why. Instead of enjoying the simple pleasures of the sky, he is swamped by letters of criticism and his office is one of charts and graphs and maps and gadgets. While you and I enjoy weather wisdom in an amateur manner, we get to look at the sky; we argue about and slosh around in hail and snow and rain and wind. We experience the weather to its fullest, and living with the weather is more rewarding than analyzing it.

Fish probably are not generally aware of the stuff they swim in any more than we are generally aware of the invisible stuff that *we* live in. But becoming aware of air is a strange and wonderful experience that certainly adds to the joy of living. I could never get to "see" atmosphere as a tangible material just by reading about it in meteorology books or by analyzing it in mathematical formulae. But once I became introduced to the sky and to that lower part of the sky which I live in, my life became very much richer. Look at it the way I do.

The New England air that I breathe in as I write these lines was somewhere over Chicago yesterday. And that very same air which I breathe out will be about five hundred miles at sea by tomorrow. The sea we live in is more like a mass of rushing rivers.

The invisible stuff around us is almost never still. Clinging to the earth by its own weight, the sun may boil it up into dense mountains but it immediately seeks its own level exactly in the manner of water; then it cascades downhill as wind, and it settles into quiet pools of calm air. But always, somewhere, there is another air mass building up, or another air mass on the move.

In my mind's eye I see the atmospheric sea as a gaseous symphony that gyrates and squirms over the surface of the earth like the changing flow of colors in oil on sunlit water. Destined never to be stagnant, the atmosphere is everlastingly stirred by giant bubbles of air that build up in still places to become what weathermen call air masses. These bubbles wobble for a while over their birthplaces and then, when they become full grown, they break away to roam across the land and crash into other kinds of air. And in their collisions, along their fronts, they create disturbances known as storms.

The discovery of these migrant bubbles of air has been one of the very few outstanding advances that man has made in the science of meteorology. Other than electronic machines of computation and communication, you will find just about the same kinds of instruments in weather stations of today that Benjamin Franklin had in his workshop more than two hundred years ago!

In fact, you can possibly outfit an amateur weather station by shopping at antique marts. You will probably find ancient but accurate barometers, psychrometers, hygrometers, and similar paraphernalia for measuring the atmosphere. Franklin was even on the track of discovering air masses when he arranged with friends in various parts of the country to keep hourly wind records so that he could later rebuild the information into a sequence of weather maps. There has never been such a pioneer of weather wisdom. His study of electricity in the atmosphere which was ended by his death has just been revived within the last decade. "It may solve the secrets of weather and storms," they say.

One of the great hopes of meteorology has materialized in rocketry, for now we can photograph the weather from above. A space vehicle can take pictures of weather happening below, as outlined by the cloud formations near the earth. But what it will really be doing is little more than just substantiating the same old weather map, plotting the positions of air masses by television and photography instead of using the slower methods of electronic communications and mapmakers.

I have drawn (as end papers inside the covers of this book) several of the air-mass "bubbles" that influence the weather in the United States. I have drawn arrows to show their habitual wanderings. By letters they are described as *cold* (P for Polar coldness) or *warm* (T for Tropical warmth), *dry* (c for continental dryness), or *wet* (a for Atlantic, p for Pacific, etc.). "cP," for example, would indicate air that is *dry* and *cold*.

I chance boring the reader with all this to explain the main character in my book, which happens to be the air mass called cP. It is born in the Northwest, in the cold, dry cradle between the Canadian Rockies and the moist barrier air of Hudson Bay. There, over the vast expanse of prairies and frozen lakes, the long nights and the absence of wind cause excessive cooling; so the dry, cold bubbles of still air called cP begins to accumulate rapidly.

You may observe cP between the lines of the following pages. In her voyage from Canada, sweeping down through the middle

United States, eastward to New England, and finally out over the Atlantic Ocean. As each person breathes her in and exhales her out, she will have become part of their existence; not just a matter of rain or shine, but a backdrop to their living moments. She will have not only become the maker of weather but the countenance of day and night, the stage and mood in which people enact their lives.

My book shall be just a collection of thoughts and instances when different people looked at the sky. Their thoughts might not have been meteorological at all. Emerson said the sky is the "daily bread of our eyes." I find this to be quite true. I have tried to be both meteorological and philosophical about the sky, but I constantly find its spiritual qualities outweighing its weather influences. I believe that the sky was created for pure beholding; that one of man's greatest joys can be simply looking at the sky.

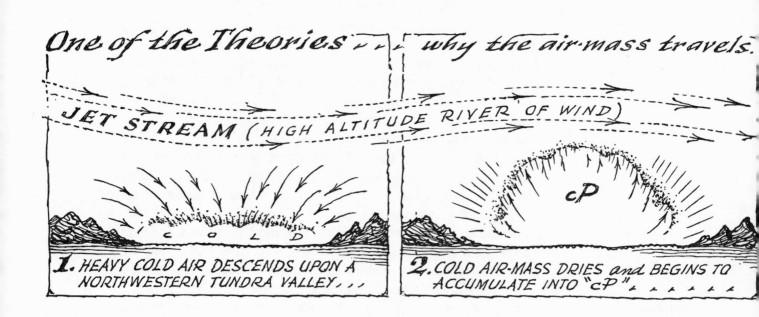

One of the Theories --- why the air-mass travels.

JET STREAM (HIGH ALTITUDE RIVER OF WIND)

cP

COLD

1. HEAVY COLD AIR DESCENDS UPON A NORTHWESTERN TUNDRA VALLEY...

2. COLD AIR-MASS DRIES and BEGINS TO ACCUMULATE INTO "cP"

What we don't know about weather could probably fill as many books as that which we do know. The men who know the most about hurricanes cannot tell you their reason for being nor can they predict their exact routes, except through guessing by past habits. Hurricane predictions are limited to the "averages method," the same method the old almanacs used. Vincent Schaefer, the famed rain maker, will tell you that no one yet knows what causes rain. The inventors of "man-made lightning" at General Electric are still trying to find out what makes real lightning. The experts on almost every phase of weather are still guessing.

When I sought the cause of cP and what triggers its voyages, I found that no two scientists agreed on any one answer, and I wonder if they shall ever know. What, I wanted to learn, periodically opens the door of America's icebox and sends that mass of

3. POLAR CANADIAN AIR-MASS (cP) BUILDS UPWARD TOWARD JET-STREAM.

4. cP IS STARTED ON ITS JOURNEY BY INFLUENCE OF JET-STREAM.

dry coldness on a fairly definite route down through Canada and eastward through the United States? Some meteorologists said it is all a matter of pressure differences; others blamed it on the turning of the earth. The most recent finding involves jet-stream[1] activity, which I go along with. Below, I have drawn that idea, which might possibly be the answer, or at least part of the answer. I'm guessing along with the experts.

[1] A jet stream is a global river of speeding air running around the earth, hugging the base of the stratosphere. Although the major northern jet stream usually flows in the middle latitude, its course varies, whipping with the rhythmic wave of a shaken rope. Possibly it (or a branch of it) periodically flows close enough to the birthplace of cP to create low pressure and suck cP into the middle latitudes, causing it to follow the course through the United States that it does.

LOOK at the SKY
... and tell the weather.

Bush Pilot

THE INLAND dryness and heavy coldness of continental polar atmosphere creates an ideal theater for aviation. Controls respond more quickly in dense atmosphere, and the lift of solid air against the wings makes take-offs shorter. It also assures slower landing speeds. I remember how the earliest planes did all their flying in the early morning or late afternoon simply to take advantage of the denseness of cooler air, and how, when I learned to fly, my take-offs and landings were never done in the thin-aired heat of midday. Some believe the flatness of the desert is the sole reason for that area being used in trials for automobile speed records; really the thinness of hot desert air enables a vehicle to shoot through it with a difference sometimes approaching an extra hundred miles an hour.

I

The Canadian bush pilot claims he can actually feel differences of the atmosphere according to temperature and humidity. Landing in tiny ponds and taking off between trees with as much as a canoe strapped to the landing gear, his awareness of the stuff he flies in must become extremely sensitive. He, if anyone, should know the qualities of cold air.

"If the meteorologists don't know what makes the cP air mass move and you really want to know," I was told, "why not ask a bush pilot? He knows just everything about Canadian weather."

It seemed logical. Flying in Northwest Territory air every day of the year, the bush pilot lives with the weather as no one else does. In place of a weather map he reads the sky. When the meteorologist says, "No," the bush pilot will be the only one out defying the weather and the weatherman. There are still a lot of people in the remote Northwest who have never seen a horse or a wheeled vehicle yet who have flown vast distances with bush pilots. The birdlike figure of one Northwest totem pole has conventional outstretched bird wings on top, but there are airplane aileron flaps on the trailing edges of the wings!

There are remote places in the tundra where very few white men have traveled, yet there are good weather records of those places as far back as thirty years ago, taken from the regular logbooks of early Canadian fliers. If anyone could offer valuable data for my cP research in the Northwest, it seemed, he might be the Canadian bush pilot.

My surmise was true. But I found that not so much Northwest wisdom comes to life in scientific papers as it does from around the big pot-bellied stoves where bush pilots swap yarns, and before I knew it I found myself collecting *yarns* instead of *scientific data.* Even Paul Bunyan couldn't improve on the folklore of the bush pilot; but the interesting part about it is that it is all true. I decided to pursue the folklore and let the better-equipped IGY men pursue science with their charts and slide rules. I'm still searching for information about what motivates cP, but I came back with a bagful of weather anecdotes.

"Who care what *makes* the weather?" said one bush pilot. "We just have to fly through the stuff! That's the big story. People like to talk about the weather: analyze it on charts and they go away bored. You just write a book about weather yarns and I'll buy it! There's a lot of stories about men and the weather that need retelling.

"Take Bill Hill, for example. He was one of the crew in an old Junkers plane that crash-landed during a Mackenzie River flight. Because of heavy snow, the ship plowed easy-like into a drift, so personal injuries were pretty slight. But the undercarriage was washed out completely and the propeller was splintered.

"Bill was an experienced bush pilot. He just looked at the sky and he said, 'According to the wind and clouds we have less than three days to do this job. If you men start to work on the undercarriage, I'll tackle the propeller.' Then he walked toward the river and he trailed its course toward the nearest settlement.

"The crew followed him as far as the bank where they had previously spotted the hulk of an abandoned boat washed up on shore. From the old boards, they decided, they might rip out enough nails and iron fittings to melt or beat into some sort of workable undercarriage. Bill, meanwhile, reached the settlement and he found himself a helper.

"The two men killed a moose and from the hide and entrails they started boiling a special glue. While the concoction boiled, fir and spruce planks were found and chopped into proper shape for duplicating an airplane propeller. A crude one was finally put together; it was laminated with the glue and chopped into shape and bored to fit a hub shaft.

"They fiitted the homemade propeller to the engine and ground-tested it right on the plane. They shaved it to a perfect balance with an old spokeshave, and some red paint gave it a final smoothness and protection from the weather.

"They stamped a smooth runway in the snow and took off with a homemade undercarriage made of split-wood skis only minutes before the start of a blizzard. They didn't have the slightest bit of trouble with the propeller: I think Bill still has the thing hanging over his fireplace.

"Experts will tell you such a feat is impossible. Bill would have told you the same thing before he did it himself. When Bill began flying in the Canadian bush, flying equipment was pretty crude stuff, so he got schooled with the rest of us in the art of improvising for survival. Even fuel and oil had to be pampered in those days. The old-time oil went hard so fast during winter that the minute your prop swung to a stop you'd have to jump out and open the petcock under the engine and let the oil out into a can before it congealed in the engine and froze stiff. You'd carry that can of oil, like the rest of your luggage, to your quarters. If you slept out, you'd put it right in your sleeping bag and keep it warm with your own body heat. When you were ready to leave, you'd bring the oil to a near boil over a fire and pour it, hot, back into the engine again.

"I remember times when I didn't have a container to drain out the oil, so I'd let it pour right out onto the snow. There it hardened into a big congealed brown lump. I'd throw that over my shoulder like a log and lug it to camp where I melted it down into a can, ready for my next take-off. Those were the days!"

There is a Canadian Indian legend that the sky was born in the north. The Eskimo will tell you in all seriousness that he lives closer to the sky than do his brothers south of him. And, oddly enough, the northern sky *is* closer; it is a scientific fact that weather and clouds occur nearer to the earth in the polar regions than they do near the equator! This is so because as the earth turns, it spins its coating of air outward by centrifugal force like a dancer's skirt. At the equator, where the atmosphere bulges out the most, clouds tower to a ten-mile height; but at the poles they hover below a five-mile mark. My drawing is necessarily exaggerated, yet this effect does exist, just as the earth itself is slightly flattened (being wider through the equator than from pole to pole). The atmosphere, therefore, is shallowest near the poles.

All too frequently in the north country flat clouds gather and sag until they lie only a few hundred feet above the land. Even then, the sky has special meaning to the north country man. He claims, for example, that during winter the earth is often reflected into such a sky and you can see miraged lakes and forests and even towns in this inverted "sky map" of the clouds. In the Arctic tundra during winter, open water beyond the horizon is reflected onto a flat cloud ceiling as a *dark* smudge (a *water sky*). And in the same manner as seen from open water, islands or icebergs over the horizon are reflected onto a flat cloud ceiling as a *bright* light (and *ice-blink*). The northland man does live closer to the sky, and he finds much more in it than one might at first imagine.

Bush pilot Everett Dane once used low cloud banks as a screen for sending a call for help. He and a copilot were freighting two live horses up the Mackenzie River. They went off course in a sudden snow flurry and when a lack of oil burned out a main engine bearing, they landed in the only open spot available, which was a frozen pond nestling within a hollow of hills. The weather closed in on them and they found themselves hopelessly lost. The horses (which are humanely rendered unconscious by injections and hog-tied for such a trip) regained consciousness and had to be untied before they kicked the fuselage through. Things looked bad.

That night Dane remembered the iceblink phenomenon and by twisting the airplane landing light upward, he hopefully flashed Morse code into the cloud banks. Luck was with him, for within a short time another spot of light from about ten miles away blinked over his head and started up a two-way conversation. Dane soon learned his location. He found that the light came from a machine shop. His engine could be repaired there. "Roger!" Dane flashed back. "Prepare for us and our disabled engine in about nine hours." And they began to dismantle the cowling.

The engine was removed from the plane and with the help

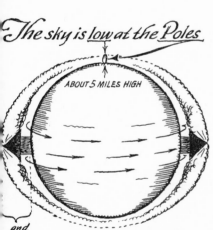

The sky is low at the Poles

ABOUT 5 MILES HIGH

and
HIGH at the EQUATOR (ABOUT 10 MILES) *because of centrifugal force.*

of a spruce-bough travois sled and made-to-order team of two horses, they hauled the engine to the outpost and had it repaired. Then the two horses pulled it back to the marooned plane and it was only a matter of hours before it was fastened back in place. The same horses were knocked out by injection again, hog-tied, and put aboard. The ship was on its way but about a week late. "You never know how handy a passenger can be on a bush flight," said pilot Dane, "especially if he's a horse."

Not long ago pilots Ed Seiler and Lee Connors set out in a light plane to get caribou. Landing on top of a treeless mountain, they bagged and skinned their catch but they found the weight was too much for the little plane. The meat was heavy, and the thin, high-altitude air couldn't lift the added load off the ground. So Seiler decided he'd fly the meat out and come back later for Connors and the gear. But when he returned, he hit a clump of grass and completely wiped out the landing gear.

There wasn't a tree for miles, but Connors had been in that kind of fix before. He picked out some good long caribou thigh

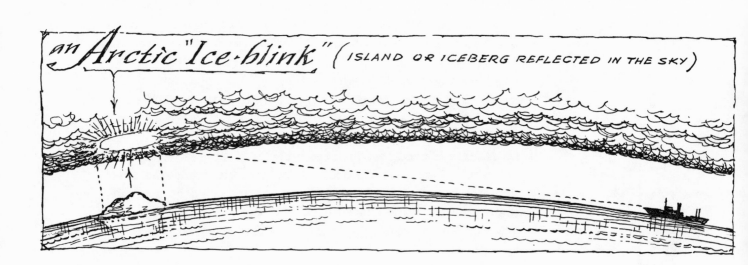

an Arctic "Ice-blink" (ISLAND OR ICEBERG REFLECTED IN THE SKY)

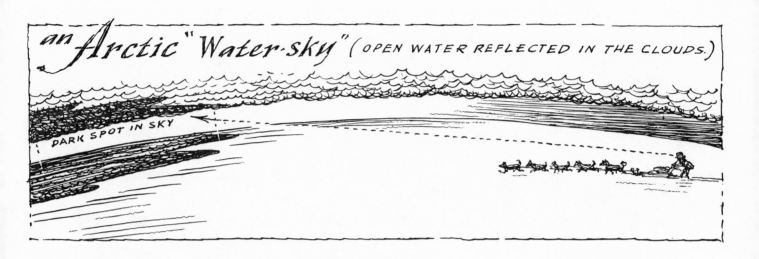

an *Arctic "Water·sky"* (OPEN WATER REFLECTED IN THE CLOUDS.)

DARK SPOT IN SKY

bones, bored them, and fastened them together into a new bone landing gear. When the plane landed at Merrill Field in Anchorage, some mechanics were just finishing lunch and one of them spotted the caribou-bone landing gear.

"My God!" he yelled. "Now I've seen everything. Here comes a flying pork chop!"

The bush pilot's tales were endless. In today's pushbutton trend, where a pilot's log looks more like a business report, flying has become starved for lore. It is good to hear such yarns.

Bush Pilot 7

Guide

THE ACTIVITIES that accompany the departure of a cold air mass from Canada are countless. No weatherman can predict the exact timing, yet most birds seem to be aware of the event even the day before. Geese that have been breeding in the still summer countryside of the Northwest, and are ready to migrate southward, mysteriously gather for flight. Although the surrounding atmosphere gives no hint of its journey, the instant the cold, dry air flow begins to tumble toward the south the birds take off.

As the air mass travels, the added pressure of mountains of cold, dense air on the land below pushes the mercury upward in barometers. It also pushes water down in the old hand-dug country wells. It tightens molecules in seasoned wood so that the furniture and beams in old houses creak and boom during the night. It presses down on the surfaces of frozen lakes and causes them to split and thunder. It pushes down on airtight cans in grocery stores, and as their lids are bent downward, it makes a clatter of little tinny sounds. It squeezes warm air upward with added vigor so that the hot smoke from campfires and chimneys shoots straight up like pillars climbing into the atmosphere.

Fish become more alert during a cP flow, swimming quickly near the surface of the water instead of lying on the bottom. Flying insects that swarm and cling and bite during low-pressure weather seem suddenly to disappear. The first hours after such a flow of weather has come through, birds are noticed flying

9

at greater heights. Because cool air is denser and therefore slower to move through, some migrating birds go up as high as a mile (where the air is thin) to make better speed. There, also, out of range of earth friction, the wind that they ride is often twice the speed of that at ground level.

In damp places, like ditches or swamps and where wood has rotted, all the stale smells that had been issuing forth into the atmosphere of low-pressure weather are suddenly pressed back again and the air is said to "smell clean." As the Indians put it, "The northwest wind is a cleaning broom that sweeps the sky."

When the cP flow is particularly strong, its upper reaches seem to attract some of the magnetized particles from the sun

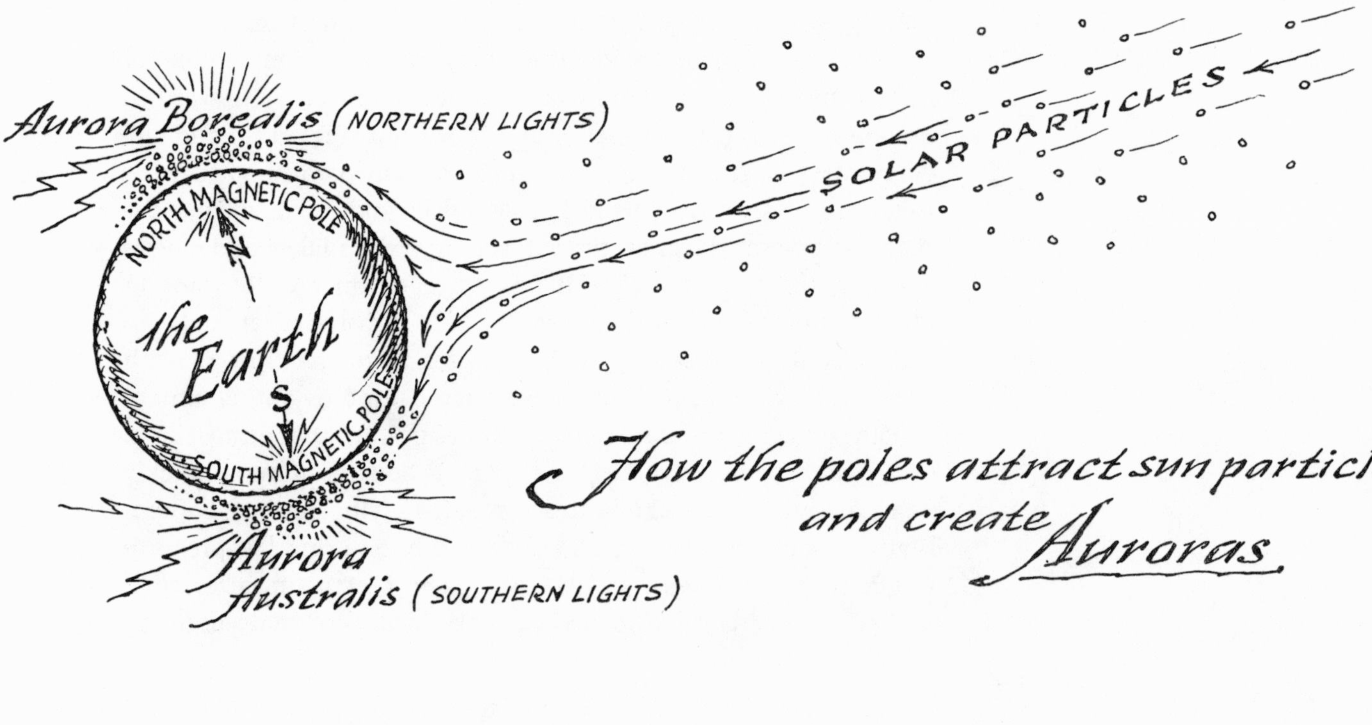

Aurora Borealis (NORTHERN LIGHTS)

NORTH MAGNETIC POLE

the Earth

SOUTH MAGNETIC POLE

Aurora Australis (SOUTHERN LIGHTS)

SOLAR PARTICLES

How the poles attract sun particles and create Auroras

that have gathered in an elliptical auroral ring above the north magnetic pole. Many weathermen claim that ionospheric aurora is too high to be attracted by weather movements so far below in the troposphere, yet during the first night of any strong polar air flow you will very frequently find some telltale glow in the northern sky over the horizon, sometimes as far south as the middle Atlantic states. During solar storms, when the sun has bombarded the earth with an extra amount of particles and the belt becomes thick and dips down toward the atmosphere, then the faint glow will take action and dart about the sky in more definite shapes. Conservationist Roy Wilcox relates such an experience while photographing birds in North Dakota: cP had just billowed over the Canadian border during the afternoon and the night air had suddenly become cold and crisp. Roy peered into the clear autumn sky from the tent opening before he tied it shut for the night.

"Great God," he said aloud. "Look at the sky!"

There, some fifty miles above the North Dakota forest, the aurora borealis had begun its silent ballet. So crescendo were the slow explosions of colored shapes that it was difficult to believe such a display could be noiseless. The aurora takes place in air so thin that even a gunshot would fail to produce sound. Yet the rustling of leaves and the moan of night wind can easily be mistaken for sounds coming from aloft. Although Roy thought he heard a faraway swishing sound, the sky above his camp was completely silent.

Roy's guide was a Canadian Indian named Pierre. He had already turned in, but Roy's remark rated no more from him than a shrug from within the sleeping bag and a turn of the head.

"Pierre knows what you see," he said. "Big north lights. They bring coldness the day after, then much wind begins. Cold air makes birds fly high. Maybe they will be too high for your camera."

"How do you know that?" asked Roy.

"In these woods we never shoot the duck or goose the day after a cold north wind comes. They all fly too high. Maybe you see some goose on his way south though. He pack up and go tomorrow. You see."

To a northland man, where the aurora is about as common as moonlight, the occurrence goes by almost unnoticed, but to Roy (a New Englander from Connecticut), such a treat was worth staying up to watch. The luminous curtains grew as bright as fire; then they hung so low that they seemed to reach the tops of the fir trees, even in danger of scorching them. Each time when the performance would die down and seem ready to end, a new ball of light would kindle and burn in the north and from it would tumble a fresh kaleidoscopic fountain of fireworks. New curtains of fire were hung in the sky. Only toward dawn did the wonderful show subside. Roy, who wouldn't think of staying up to see a late, late show on television, found himself still watching the show in the sky as the first rays of day lit the eastern horizon.

Exactly as Pierre had predicted, the new day was colder and a sudden wind flowed from the north. And just as Pierre had said, the birds *were* flying higher. Flocks of ducks that ordinarily cruised at about a hundred feet were skirting the morning horizon at close to a thousand feet.

Roy surveyed the countryside as breakfast coffee was brewing, marveling at Pierre's weather predictions. His eyes wandered to the clear skies directly above. If he had been looking for it, he would never have found it, but high overhead he saw the tiniest of dots.

"Come here, Pierre," Roy called, "and look at this. It seems too high to be a bird, yet it circles like one. What do you think it is?"

Pierre left the chores of the campfire and squinted upward until the folds of brown skin on his face hid his eyes.

"Leader goose," he said. "He waits for goose flock on way south. You watch and you see. Pretty soon they all come."

Coffee was finished and things were packed in the canoe, but the dot still circled overhead. Surely there was a high wind at that altitude, possibly fifty knots. Yet the bird did not drift at all; his navigation was absolutely perfect.

Just before breaking camp, Roy heard the faraway melody of geese in flight and looked upward, but they were still too distant to see. Within a minute the gaggle came into sight. There was a long, irregular line moving slowly from the north at a great height, and heading directly toward the dot overhead. It seemed a good five minutes before the geese reached the circling bird, but when they did, they all fluttered out of formation and

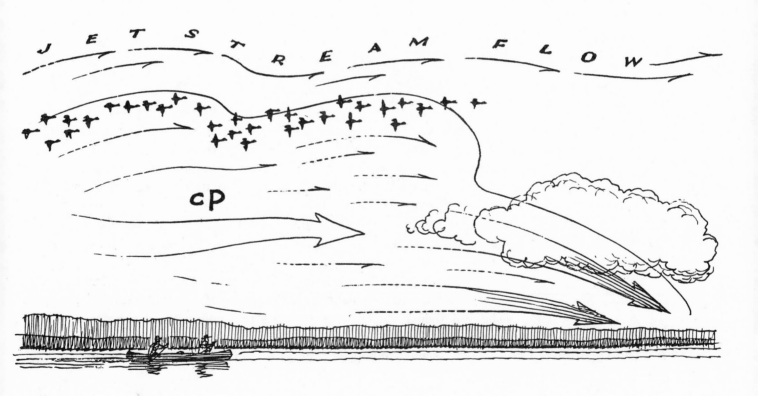

into a temporary halt as if in some brief handshaking sort of conversation. Roy, who watched it all through binoculars, lost the lone bird in the swarm of other dots in the sky. But without a loss of ten seconds the flight resumed formation, this time in a fine, V-shaped wedge, and continued on its way southward. The lone goose had joined the group; now (according to Pierre's prediction) he was leading it southward. Abroad the speeding river of dense cP air the gaggle disappeared into the haze above the southern horizon.

What telepathic knowledge had put that one bird aloft in the very spot where the flight would pass? How full the sky must be, Roy thought, filled with messages that only wildlife can perceive.

"It seemed impossible," he said later, "that the goose could be told the flight would come through at that very spot, altitude, and time of day. The migration seemed to be timed to take advantage of the southeasterly flowing wind all right, but how would one lone bird hundreds of miles away be so prompted? Yet when I stop to think about it, I remember that in each square inch of that remote territory there were also a thousand messages of man, everything from news broadcasts to soap operas and TV pictures, too. So I guess it's not so impossible, after all."

Clergyman

A COLD air mass on the march generally travels faster than a warm air mass; it is natural that it kicks up more of a fuss along its collision front. Especially on flatland stretches, where the storm can gain speed, do squall lines and roll clouds build up along a cold front. In the warm air of late autumn and on toward afternoon, when the heat of day has built up a special invitation to any oncoming mass of cool air, concentrated thunderstorms will form all along a cold front. Often there will be thunderheads about ten to twenty miles apart; it might pour torrents in one place while in between the thunderheads there will be no rain at all.

The frontal zone of cP passed through North Dakota on Friday, and it entered South Dakota on a Saturday during county fair time. Midmorning broke with clear skies and a few scraggly cirrus clouds riding lazily overhead. It looked promising. But as the heat of day increased, the warm earth sent up streams of hot air from the flat plains which at three thousand feet burst into shaggy cumulus clouds. By noon these clouds had lowered and darkened enough to be definite forebearers of rain. By two hours after midday cP had pushed up thunderous "shell-burst" clouds and an occasional cumulo-nimbus appeared over the horizon.

"Damnation!" said Haynes to Father Donohue as they leaned over the county fair racetrack and watched the sky. "My horse is due to run in fifteen minutes and will you just look at that horizon! Honey Girl never set foot on a wet track before; she'll lose sure as you're a foot high! Mame and I've gone and put up every cent we had in the savings account to win this race. And what do we get but a storm!"

Far to the north of the fair grounds a sulphury thunderhead

had formed and lightning was already flickering from its innards. A low cannonade of thunder could be heard whenever the noise of the crowds lessened. Far to the south was another storm center; it, too, looked threatening.

Father Donohue looked at the two storm centers and stroked his chin in an attitude of intense thought, as he does when he is about to make a profound observation in the pulpit.

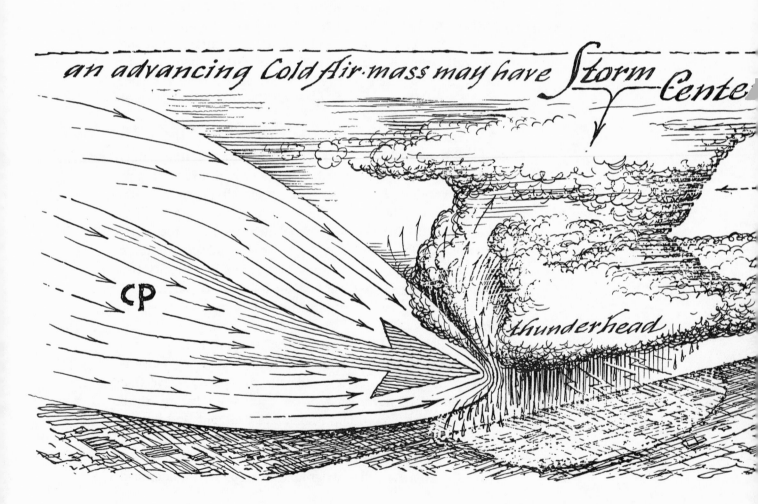

an advancing Cold Air·mass may have Storm Cente

CP

thunderhead

"Haynes," he said, "I don't think it's fixin' to rain at all. You just stop worrying and take my word for it."

"Look here, Father," said Haynes. "I have good respect for your weather prophetin' but I sure know a storm when I see one. I'd say that storm should hit here in about ten minutes. Me and Mame are going to lose every cent that we've saved up for ten years, and you want me to stop worrying."

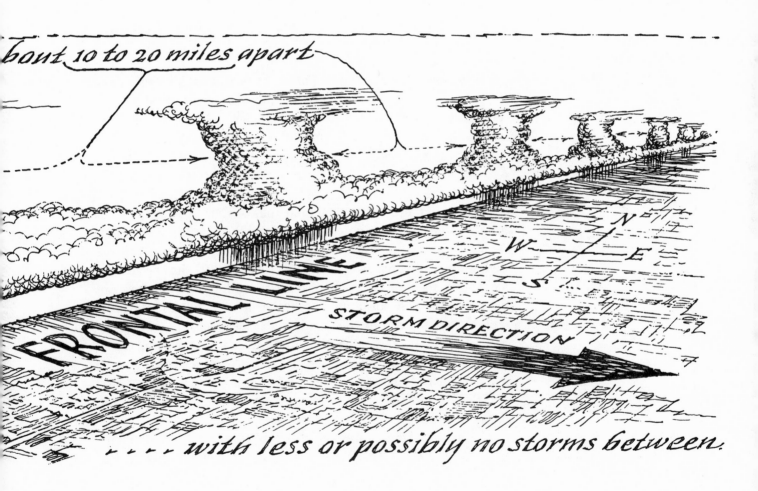

"I'll tell you what I'll do," said Father Donohue. "I don't bet on horses because town folks wouldn't like that. But I'll bet you a fifty-dollar contribution toward the new parish-house fund. I'll bet you that Honey Girl runs on a dry track. Furthermore, I'll bet you that the storm doesn't hit here at all but that it will go past! What do you say?"

"By gosh, Father, I'll take you up on that! If Honey Girl runs on a dry track she'll win for sure. And if she wins, I'll never miss the fifty bucks! Are you sure you want to do it?"

An hour later, at the refreshment stand, Haynes counted out five crisp tens from a fat wad of bills.

"It sure beats me how you knew that storm would go by!" he said. "But I'm darn glad it did. Honey Girl never run a better race."

"Thanks, Haynes," said Father Donohue as he stuffed the folded tens into a packet beneath his black coat, "but all the credit goes to the Bible. If you'll look far enough into that remarkable book, you'll find just about anything you're looking for. You should try it some time."

"It sure told you how to win a bet," said Haynes. "How did you do it?"

"Yes, it did just that. The Bible tells us that God's fury moves in a straight route and seldom falls on those in the side lines. Well, I just see lightning as one of God's furies. When you see lightning in the north or south as we did, and the storms are coming from the west, as almost all autumn storms do, you can be sure they will continue to move in a straight easterly route and that you're not in their path but in between. It's only lightning from a westerly direction that you have to watch. Christ tells you: 'When ye see a cloud rise out of the west, straightway ye say: There cometh a shower; and so it is.' (Luke 12:54.) Yes, sir, the Lord was a pretty good all-around weatherman. The best, I might add."

Haynes squinted and smiled doubtfully at Father Donohue. "I don't know whether you're kidding me or not, but I'll just bet on you from now on. What does the Bible say about tomorrow's weather?" he added with a chuckle.

But Father Donohue took the jibe seriously. He stroked his chin and looked toward the horizon where the sun was lowering behind the fairground stables. The heavens were a sort of peach crimson, with an upper sky of solid cirrus fibers that blazed a brilliant red from the setting sun.

"First-rate day as I see it," he said. "There's not the slightest chance of any rain tomorrow. Now, if a sunrise looked like that sunset, you could be sure it would rain in about ten hours."

"I suppose the Bible tells you that, too," said Haynes.

"That it does," answered Father Donohue. "Matthew, Chapter 16."

That night Haynes told his wife about the race, about the bet, and how Father Donohue predicted the movement of the storm.

"You say that he told you it wouldn't rain tomorrow? That's good news because the Ladies' Aid is having an afternoon social in the Perkins' orchard and we sure hope it's goin' to be clear. What chapter did he say?" she asked as she reached beneath the table for the family Bible.

"I think he said Matthew, Chapter 16. What does it say there?"

Mame thumbed through the old book and finally stopped at one page. She read carefully to herself, and then looking over her glasses to be sure that Haynes was listening, she began to read aloud.

" 'When it is evening,' " she read, " 'ye say, It will be fair weather, for the sky is red. And in the morning: Today *there will be a storm,* for the sky is red and lowering.' "

"Those words," said Mame as she closed the book, "were spoken by Jesus Christ."

"Well, I'll be damned!" said Haynes.

Weatherman

WINTER IS so persistent in the northwest plains that the Indians called them "Pahoja" or land of gray snow. Void of trees, the flatlands of Nebraska are perhaps more open to weather than any other state. The ground is weathered and seasoned by long winters into a tight sod suitable for instant building material; the settlers sawed it directly from the ground and built their sod houses with this "Nebraska brick." Nowhere can a man look farther without seeing anything (according to Will Rogers) and nowhere does a man live closer to the sky. Canadian air flows into Nebraska slowly, but there it meets the pull of strong jet streams and accelerates to gale-force wind.

Near the geographical center of the nation, Nebraska is a mixing bowl for many great air masses. Some of them pass through, while some end their journey to disintegrate by mixing with other kinds of air. The damp, cool air of Polar Pacific (pP) often ends its voyage over the middle plains, and the hot, dry southwest air from the desert country (cT) pays a token call every other week. The strong, wet flow of warm Gulf air (gT) comes up the Mississippi Valley, and cP is a rowdy visitor that usually brushes through the northeast part of Nebraska to make the temperature drop there. The whole lot of air masses can keep a weatherman on the jump to forecast the results of such an atmospheric concoction. Before the time of TV and radio, the Nebraskan farmer kept his weatherman's phone busy most of the time. They used to send meteorologists out there just for the experience. If you could predict Nebraska weather, they used to say, and keep up with the Midwest farmer's phone calls, you were a pro. One of meteorology's favorite stories is about the new weath-

23

erman who was sent from New York to Nebraska. One of his first calls was from a farmer who wanted to butcher his hogs.

"Will it be cold enough tomorrow morning," he asked, "to kill my hogs?"

"I don't know much about hogs," answered the new weatherman. "But if your hogs can't stand the cold, you'd better take them inside tonight—tomorrow's going to be colder."

Another call came from a farmer who flew his own airplane and wanted to get information on the cloud conditions.

"You the new weatherman in Omaha?" he asked.

"Yes, sir, I am. What can I do for you?"

"Well, I'd like to know how high the ceiling is there."

"Well, I've not measured it yet," replied the new man as he looked up from his desk, "but I'd guess it's about eight feet."

Another call came through from a farmer complaining about a sudden snowfall.

"There are about a thousand barrels of snow out on my corn field," he said. "What do you think is the cause of that?"

"That doesn't sound like too much snow for this time of year," the weatherman replied, "but I've never heard it measured by the barrelful!"

"I'm not *measuring* the snow," the farmer said, "I mean it's *shaped* like barrels."

Barrels of snow. *(snow rollers on a Nebraska farmland).*

What had fallen on the farmer's land was soft snow over a layer of old hard snow and whipped into "snow rollers." If the wind is strong and the grade a very gentle slope downward, new snow is sometimes rolled into muff-like shapes. A snow roller ranges from egg size to giant barrel size, according to the snow condition and the force of the wind.

At Potter, Nebraska, during a passage of cold air from the north, unusually large hailstones fell to earth and then the weatherman's phone really began to ring. Hail was coming down larger than baseballs! One stone was measured as being seventeen inches in circumference and it had a weight of one and a half pounds.[1] Near Grand Isle, in 1959, a hailstorm left an eighteen-inch layer of hailstones over a fifteen-mile area; some of those stones were three and a half inches in diameter. This time the weatherman's phone didn't ring. The lines were out.

In the 1920's an Omaha newspaper editor named Kane was predicting weather with uncanny accuracy while the new county meteorologist was doing pretty badly. The new weatherman didn't know the editor but, using an anonymous name, he thought he might chance a telephone call.

"My name is Smith," he said, "and I'd like to know how you manage to predict the weather the way you do."

"It's simple," replied Kane. "We have a new meteorologist out here and I just wait till I hear what he predicts, then I predict the opposite."

What the Nebraska weatherman watches out for mostly is the clash between cP and gT. When the dry, cold air from the north hits the warm air from the south, things begin to happen because then all the atmospheric differentials become extreme. This clashing of opposite atmospheres makes the whole Mississippi Valley a playground for line-squall thunderstorms and in spring for those parasites of such storms, the tornadoes.

[1] It was weighed on a drugstore scale and the affidavit notarized by a local lawyer.

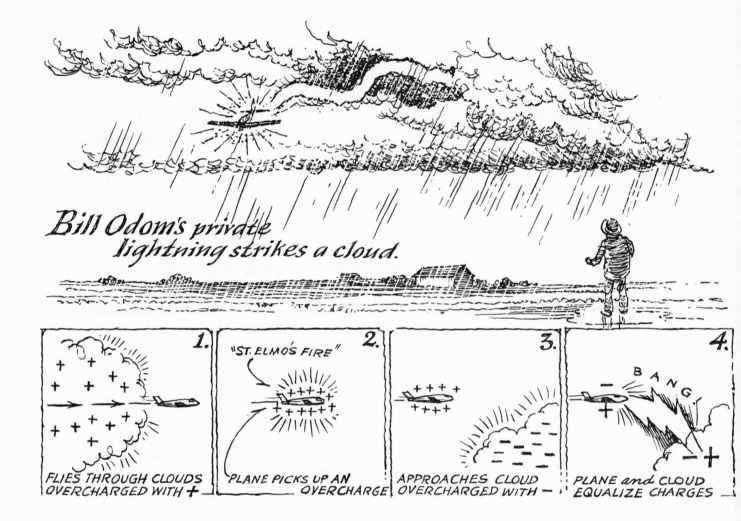

Bill Odom's private lightning strikes a cloud.

1. FLIES THROUGH CLOUDS OVERCHARGED WITH +

2. "ST. ELMO'S FIRE" PLANE PICKS UP AN OVERCHARGE

3. APPROACHES CLOUD OVERCHARGED WITH —

4. BANG PLANE *and* CLOUD EQUALIZE CHARGES

The weatherman at Omaha airport once received two interesting calls during a sudden cold-front storm. He told me that one was from a farmer who had seen a "gray, twin-motor airplane flying low, all on fire." A few minutes later a call came in from a farmer who saw a "gray, twin-motor plane flying low, struck by lightning." Such a twin-motor plane, piloted by Bill Odom, had left the airport in the face of the storm, so the airport became worried and immediately tried to contact it. No reply. They waited dismally for some word of disaster to come through, but no such word ever did come through: Odom's plane was completely silent.

It was about a year later that Bill Odom and I were chatting before my fireside at Roslyn, Long Island, and the subject of St. Elmo's fire came up.

"I can tell you something about St. Elmo's," said Bill. "It happened to me as I took off right after a cold air mass came through. The electrical differential in the air set up such a clatter that my radio became useless almost before I'd left the ground, so I switched it off.

"At about seven thousand feet the differential between my ship and the surrounding air became so great that the charge was flowing out of my wing tips like orange flames. I thought if I flew lower I could shake the stuff off, but at two thousand it got worse: my propeller arc became a sheet of flame. I'd never seen anything like it. I'd heard about St. Elmo's fire before and I knew what to expect. I put on dark glasses and I sat there waiting for the plane to discharge its load into some passing cloud. And then, suddenly, it happened. A bolt of lightning connected the right wing of the plane with a cloud and it sounded like a cannon going off. The flash was bad even through my dark glasses, and for the next few minutes I was flying blind. After the discharge, I switched my radio on and found it had quieted down. Everything was back to normal."

"That didn't happen near Omaha, did it?" I asked.

Weatherman 27   "Well, I'll be darned," said Bill. "How did *you* know?"

Parachutist

cP SWUNG eastward into Iowa. On both sides of the river of cool air vast pools of low pressure formed in the atmosphere, shrouded by oceans of stratus clouds. The weatherman called the weather "uncertain," and he talked of scattered centers of light showers. It was "that kind of day."

When the sky gathers into a ceiling of cobwebs to overcast the day with the promise of rain, a certain stillness takes over. During this dull sequence of weather, existence seems to pass slower: the whole day becomes immersed in a mood of waiting. Tree leaves that ordinarily dance in the sun, and grass that waves in the wind, become still. On such a day birds roost rather than exert themselves by flying through the thin air of lowering pressure. Rabbits pose by the side of the road until you are almost upon them before they move off.

"A gray sky," so the Iowa farmers say, "makes time go slow to wait before the storm winds blow."

Even sounds respond differently before the rain. They seem to reach your ear slowly, and all the distant sounds of the countryside come to you as if heard down a long corridor. Elijah said, "There is a sound of abundance of rain," and Franklin's Almanack said, "Sound traveling far and wide, a day of rain will soon betide." They were speaking of such a day as this.

Thor Anderson stopped hoeing his garden to view the day and to sense its mood. The air was still except for the low drone of a faraway plane.

People used to say that a locomotive whistle could "sound like rain"; now they may say the same thing about the noise of an airplane. Clear, yet as if in a distant dream, an airplane's sleepy buzz seems to beat against the lowering backdrop of gray clouds and make the echo-like sound that always foretells rain.

Thor rested his wrists on the butt of his hoe and he squinted 29 at the black dot in the sky. To him, the drone of a plane was the most melancholy of all sounds, for it brought memories of his son Aaron. Most times he pretended not to hear. Sometimes he worked the ground all the harder in an effort to beat away such thoughts of sadness and death.

Aaron had been a good farm boy. Like others of the early nineteen twenties who were "bitten by the gasoline bug," he'd spent a lot of time tinkering with engines. But he never let it interfere with the farm chores. At sixteen Aaron could almost take apart and put together again a Model-T engine blindfolded.

At the county fair you could always find Aaron near the motor racetrack or watching the mechanics work on the OX-5s and Hispano-Suizas that powered the biplanes that flew in the air show. Second to his own field of corn there was nothing more beautiful to Aaron than a gasoline engine. And in a matter of time the field of corn took second place.

As on most farms, decisions in the Anderson family were made only after careful thought and planning. So when Aaron said that he wanted to fly, even to have an airplane of his own, Thor did not object. He knew that his boy had given it sound deliberation.

"After all, other farm boys have gone into flying," Thor would tell Mama Anderson as if he were thinking aloud and trying to convince himself. "Some of them, so the papers say, have built their own airplanes!"

By the fall of 1925 Aaron had bought himself an airplane engine. Boxed in its original crate, it was a World War I surplus engine that sold for only two hundred dollars. Aaron put it in one of the barns near the south field and by gradually moving out all the farm equipment there was finally nothing inside but the OX-5 in its crate.

Then Aaron made a wind sock for the roof of the barn. "It is a good thing for a farmer," Aaron told his father, "to know exactly which way the wind is blowing." Soon people referred to the barn as "Aaron's hangar," and they were sure that some- day it would house a complete airplane.

The south-field crops had been rotated so that corn came up every third year; but corn made for a field of bumpy rows and was not the sort of surface on which to land an airplane. So corn went to the other fields and the south field only grew grass for hay. When the field was new mown and the wind sock on the barn was blowing in the breeze, Aaron often lingered just to look at the sight, and Thor knew his boy was visualizing the plane-to-be taking off and landing there.

For nearly two years Aaron saved toward that day when he could buy his own airplane. Surplus engines were easy to come by but airframes were scarce. They were either crashed jobs that were ready to be junked or they were good enough to be bought quickly by the barnstormers. So Aaron was patient. He took lessons in flying at the local airport and saved a little money that he earned doing odd jobs around the hangars. Twice he earned a hundred dollars by making parachute jumps at the county fair.

Aaron told no one about his jumps until after they were done. Actually, he related, it wasn't dangerous at all. "It's no more than jumping from the hayloft and landing in the hay below." But the word got around that Aaron was a "daredevil parachute jumper" and people used to point out the barn with the wind sock as they went by, saying, "That's where Aaron Anderson, the daredevil, lives." When Aaron went to town on a Saturday, there were always a few young boys who asked him for his autograph. Then he would sign his name in a broad scrawl ending it with a flourish and a little sketch of a parachute with a man dangling from it.

The afternoon when Aaron died was blue-skied and clear. It was perfect visibility for the air show, yet the plane that the contestants jumped from was so high that you couldn't see it, well over twelve thousand feet. In those days twelve thousand feet was a good ceiling for any plane; at that height the big wooden propeller was already grasping desperately for a bite into the thin air and the plane would flounder.

Parachutist *31*

It was the custom in delayed-chute contests for each jumper to carry a small sack of flour with him which he would rip open when he left the plane. That made a cloud of white that streamed through the blue sky and marked his position for the audience.

"If you will keep your eyes aloft," said the announcer, "you will see three puffs of white. Keep your eyes on them, ladies and gentlemen, and you will soon see three little black dots: those will be the contestants themselves. The one who opens his chute *last* wins!"

The crowd was hushed until several people pointed upward. "There! There they are!" Three tiny lines of white appeared high aloft, and after what seemed an unduly long time the three men came into view. But they were dots that seemed to hang motionless for so long a time that people went back to talking and laughing, and hawkers began selling hot dogs. People resumed eating with just an occasional glance upward.

The human body falls faster and faster in a free fall, until it reaches a maximum velocity of about 140 miles an hour. But as you near the ground where the air is thicker you are "slowed down," and not that it would really make much difference, your body would strike the earth going only 125 m.p.h.

Aaron won the contest easily. When his chute opened he was only about thirty feet from the ground. The thud of his body was heard distinctly by everyone in the grandstand, and it was a fearful sound that lingered long in one's memory. The prize that would have bought a Curtiss JN-4D airframe that Aaron had a cash deposit on, paid for his burial instead.

Thor often wondered what Aaron might have thought about on his way down through the sky. Perhaps he thought about the farm and his mother and father. Perhaps he thought about the OX-5 in the barn. Perhaps he was thinking of nothing more than just the jump itself and the way the air cushioned him from below and felt like a solid. "You can reach right out and grab the air," he often said when he told about parachuting. "It's the real thrill of jumping!"

Thor often recalled Aaron's words when he was alone in the fields, particularly when he felt the first blast of a rain squall as it swept across the countryside. At that instant when you might stop to admire the oncoming storm, he would stretch out his hands to feel the wind pass between his fingers.

There are a great many things that bring memories of his boy to Thor, but most of them come from the sky. It might be the whine of the wind or the drone of some faraway plane. Of course there is still the stand of grass in the south field, and the barn with the wind sock on it, and inside there is the engine in a crate addressed "To: Aaron Anderson."

Private Flyer

OVER THE flat country of western Illinois the dense air of cP can shovel under warm air from the Gulf and push it skyward with amazing velocities. Each cumulus puff of cloud is some evidence of a vertical wind. Most of us think of wind as being horizontal, and here, next to the earth, that is about the only thing that wind can be. But the flier aloft moves in winds from all directions and his altimeter becomes a weather vane for those winds that go up and down.

Gill Robb Wilson, who looks at the sky more than the average man does, told me about a vertical wind which he shall always remember. His work of running *Flying Magazine* calls for many a quick trip by air, and his file of aerial anecdotes is a full one.

"I was flying over flat farm country," Gill recalls, "when I ran past a sudden cold-front disturbance. The updrafts became so strong that I found my altimeter clocking off altitude although my plane was in a horizontal position, sometimes even though it was in a dive.

"As I flew through the whizzing remnants of thunderclouds, my thoughts went back to wartime days when the little ships of World War I would have been all but battered by such buffeting. I recalled how those frail biplanes were at the mercy of the slightest storm and how we were sometimes tossed to heights that called for oxygen which we didn't have in those days. As the motor hummed and the scud clouds continually whipped past the cockpit of my Fairchild, the hypnotic effect lulled me into a pleasant trance which brought back many of the old times. I became deep in thought. I so imagined myself back in those days that I automatically scanned the sky ahead for an enemy plane.

"And then, in a flash, I seemed doomed as I awoke from my daydreaming. Diving on me from a wisp of gray cloud and too

35

close for any possibility of avoiding collision I caught the silhouette of an apparition out of the long past—a Fokker D-VIII airplane. There was no mistaking the awkward lines of the old German fighter with its snub nose and its stubby vertical fin.

"A surprisingly small impact came almost with the instant of recognition—a very slight jar and a crack appearing down the left side of my Fairchild windshield. And that was all.

"Was I dead? Was I dreaming? Was my mind disarranged? I whipped into a vertical bank, searching the ground and sky for some explanation. Nothing. I tested myself for reflexes. I tested the flight and engine controls. The plane still droned on safely and the only tangible evidence that anything at all had occurred beyond some possible mental illusion was that crack in the windshield. I traced it down with my fingernail, half-expecting it to prove only a streak of rain. But it was a crack all right.

"Where would a Fokker D-VIII come from? There probably wasn't one such aircraft left in the world. Could it have been something resembling a Fokker? My mind ran over all the aircraft types I could think of with comparative lines. Nothing. And even if it had been any other aircraft than a Fokker, how could I have seen it in such proximity without having my plane demolished by collision?

"I can tell you that when I sat down on my flight strip I was about as bewildered as a presumed sane pilot could get. The attendant came out to take over my Fairchild, and he waved a friendly hello and looked me over.

" 'Get out and look here,' he called, as the prop spun to a halt. He was pointing toward the right wing.

"I clambered out and looked to where he was pointing. There in the leading edge of the wing was a frayed hole about the size of a derby hat. Bits of fabric and balsa wood were protruding. He reached into the aperture and pulled out what was unmistakably the debris of a power model aircraft, a Fokker D-VIII!

" 'I'm not dead. I'm not dreaming. I'm not crazy,' I observed to him.

"'Well, at least you're not dead or dreaming,' he agreed, 'but what happened?'

"I described it.

"'You were flying too low,' he said. 'I guess you must have been bounced down by a downdraft.'

"I denied it. 'I was around six thousand feet and still rising when I hit that model,' I insisted.

"'No model could climb to that height,' he said.

"Eventually we learned what had happened. A group at the airport had been flying their scale models when the cP air mass came through. As the heavy, cold air snowplowed beneath the lighter, warmer air, it had sent up powerful blasts of vertical wind. The D-VIII model was sucked up in one and lost to view when the storm struck, carrying it to six thousand feet. It was doing acrobatics on its own and still rising, a full five miles away from the airport, when it had tried to bring me down. My depth perception is pretty good: but with no visual reference at all, and the whole thing happening so quickly, it certainly looked like the full-sized job but a few yards farther away.

"Even bad weather, I thought, can be good: I blessed the storm. It had brought back to me a memory of the rich past. All the old Luftwaffe pilots in Valhalla would be chortling to themselves. Maybe such as my kid brother, Dave Putnam, Ernie Giroux, Roaul Lufbury, and Bud Lehr, and a host of others were grinning at me, with their helmets and goggles pushed back on their heads in the old carefree manner. God bless weather, *all weather*, good and bad!"

I have often thought of Gill Robb Wilson's blessing "all weather, good and bad." And when I hear someone remark, "Boy, isn't *this* a lousy day?" I have devised a stock retort: "Sure," I reply, "but isn't it a *wonderful* lousy day?"

Cloud anatomy of a
Cold front storm.

ANV

Cumulo
nimb

"SCUD·CLOUDS"-AN
AFTERMATH OF
RAGGED STORM
REMNANTS.

Advance of cooler air

RAIN

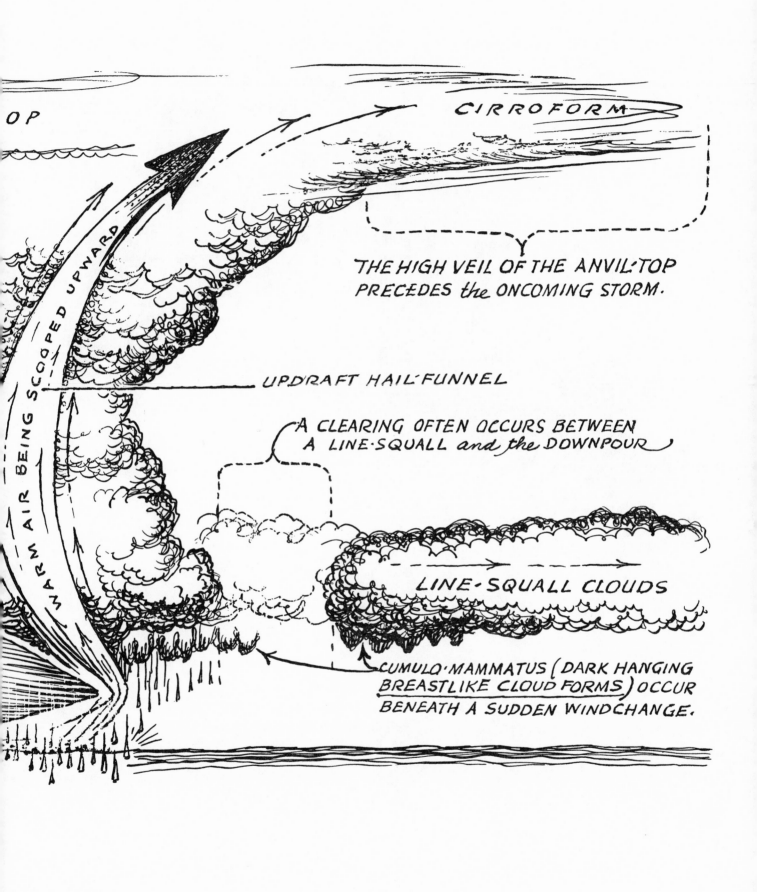

OP

CIRROFORM

THE HIGH VEIL OF THE ANVIL-TOP PRECEDES *the* ONCOMING STORM.

UPDRAFT HAIL-FUNNEL

A CLEARING OFTEN OCCURS BETWEEN A LINE-SQUALL *and the* DOWNPOUR

WARM AIR BEING SCOOPED UPWARD

LINE-SQUALL CLOUDS

CUMULO-MAMMATUS (DARK HANGING BREASTLIKE CLOUD FORMS) OCCUR BENEATH A SUDDEN WINDCHANGE.

Sign-painter

PEOPLE HAVE said that in the face of death "their whole life paraded" before them. I believe the explanation of this is that during one split second their mind was just working full throttle —that they were in a profound state of complete "awakeness" and *awareness*. I believe that man's mind is seldom entirely awake; that if it were so for a full ten minutes the effect would be exhausting. I do know that even one slight instant of complete awareness can become so indelible that it stays with you always, and that the calmest mood or the slightest sound or the most subtle odor can be so poignant as to be recalled years later. Weather can impress me in that manner; a certain brightness of day or exceptional taste of atmosphere can often carry me back to some like instant that occurred during my childhood.

I had forgotten that I had ever been in Indiana. Suddenly, now as I sat before my typewriter to write about Indiana, I remembered. I recalled an instant thirty-five years ago, near Kokomo, when I was a traveling sign painter, traveling in a Model-T Ford.

I was young enough to think that sleeping in a hayloft was fun. I clearly remember the coldness and how toward morning I regretted not having taken advantage of the offer of a quilt.

"It's going to be a fine night," I had told the farmer, "and the hay will keep me plenty warm."

I'd done a good day's work, and the soft resting place was most inviting. Before the light of day had given out I'd outlined on the side of the barn and partly filled in with orange and black paint the sentiment "YOU'LL TREAT YOURSELF TO THE BEST IF YOU CHEW MAIL POUCH." It was good to rest.

41

As the chill of night became stronger, I burrowed deeper into the hay. And then at one moment (or perhaps it was a split second!) I had the awareness of extraordinary comfort. Being so surrounded by the presence of a past summer and the perfume of meadow grass, hearing the stirring and breathing of the farm animals below, feeling the security of the immense barn and ancient beams all around me, the awareness of comfort became one of those unforgettable memories. Now, after so many years of observation and weather study, the experience means more to me. I recall the time of year, the farm scene and the weather, and the whole recollection becomes that much richer.

A Canadian air mass had probably passed through at that time, for the full heat of an Indiana autumn day had radiated into space and the atmosphere which hours ago had been a cauldron of bubbling thermals had suddenly become still.

A cold wave that moves in upon autumn night air always meets the least resistance. There are no updrafts to burst into thunderhead clouds; there are no ingredients for wind squalls or rain torrents or lightning. There is just a dropping of temperature and the occurrence of all the little things that go with a sudden change. These are the things that go unnoticed except to the countryman.

Frogs become quiet. Spiders forsake their webs and insects seek refuge from the cold. Crickets slacken their cadence in exact rhythm with the temperature drop. Katydids that have already reduced their triple summer call to a double autumn call of "Kate-ee!" now give forth with a single muffled "kate!" (At 40 degrees they and all other insects become mute.)

The sudden weight of high-pressure air is said to irritate the sensitive ears of bats; instead of skimming the ponds, they are seen flying high over the trees where the air pressure is a bit lower. Swallows, too, fly higher, with the added reason that their meal of insects is elevated too.

The bark on old trees tightens in the drier air, and there are a thousand little snapping sounds in the forest. Telephone wires

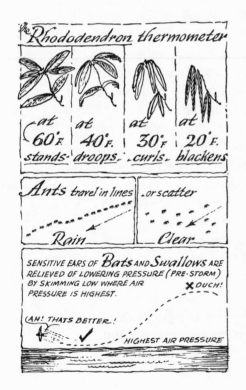

The Rhododendron thermometer

at 60°F. stands· at 40°F. droops· at 30°F. curls· at 20°F. blackens

Ants travel in lines ·or scatter
Rain   Clear

SENSITIVE EARS OF Bats AND Swallows ARE RELIEVED OF LOWERING PRESSURE (PRE-STORM) BY SKIMMING LOW WHERE AIR PRESSURE IS HIGHEST.   ✗ OUCH!

(AH! THATS BETTER!)
HIGHEST AIR PRESSURE

Dew

A HEAVY DEW COLLECTS EARLY IN FAIR NIGHT AIR. NO DEW, SIGN OF A RAIN.

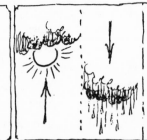

Clouds

LOWER AS MOISTNESS OF A LOW PRESSURE AREA OF A STORM APPROACHES.

Leaves
WHITISH

SHOW THEIR BACKS WHEN NON-PREVAILING (STORM) WIND BLOWS THEM OVER.

Insects

SWARM BEFORE A RAIN, CLING AND BITE MOST WHEN ATMOSPHERE IS MOIST

Smoke

RISES SLOWER OR EVEN CURLS DOWNWARD WHEN PRE-STORM WINDS BLOW.

Odors

PREVIOUSLY CAPTIVE IN HIGH PRESSURE, FLOW OUT IN PRE-RAIN LOW PRESSURE.

Birds

FLY HIGHER DURING THE HIGH PRESSURE AIR OF FAIR WEATHER SKIES.

Halos

OCCUR WHEN SUN OR MOON SHINE THROUGH ICE CLOUDS OF APPROACHING RAINSTORM.

shrink: their dried poles become giant sounding boards for a shrill Aeolian hum that you can hear all along the highway.

Rhododendron leaves curl to the proper angle corresponding with the temperature. The sky becomes steely black; stars that are ordinarily too faint to see suddenly become visible in the cleared atmosphere. The air across the landscape becomes heavy with coldness and it slides downhill exactly like water, settling in the low places as pools of white mist.

Around the farm during a night chill there is a sudden stir among the animals. The old rived shingles on the barn roof creak as they shrink and curl. The big hand-hewn beams crack and boom as their fibers tighten and their wooden-pegged joints shift in accordance with the change. The still of the barnyard is broken as the windmill swings around to face the wind.

The added pressure of dense air pushes the more pungent farm odors back into the rotting manure and damp hay so that the atmosphere becomes clean and sweet-smelling. The country-man's life is rich with such weather lore, but a cold spell during autumn is particularly abundant with signs.

Indiana is an open country with more valleys or pockets than hills; the early highways used to stretch straight over the flat-lands and suddenly drop out of sight as they dipped into pock-ets to bridge across the "cricks." The bridges, of course, were wooden and covered. Even now there are more covered bridges in Indiana than there are in the whole "covered-bridge state" of Vermont.[1] When I worked in Indiana as a sign painter I am sure there must have been more than a thousand covered bridges there. The old-timers wouldn't let me paint signs on many of the bridge sides "because the paint might rot the wood." Of course I tried to tell them how "paint preserves wood." Yet they were quite right in their own weather wisdom: the oldest covered bridges standing in America happen to be the ones that have never been

[1] At the writing of this book there were about 150 covered bridges in Indiana and 120 in Vermont.

The old covered bridges breathed with the weather.

Camber

painted—the ones where the raw wood was allowed to weather and season in moving air. Wherever moisture gets under paint and becomes trapped, I find, wood is doomed to decay.

"These bridges have to breathe," one town official told me, "and that's why we don't want any paint on them to stop that important process. A covered bridge is like a giant barometer: when the pressure goes up and down, so does the curve of the bridge. Not much, mind you, but enough for a good bridge man to see. A bridge is a barometer, too: when the wood dries, down goes the curve again. You have to keep the right amount of moisture in a wooden truss to keep that gentle upsweep in place.

'Some folks think they cover bridges to keep the snow out. Time was when they had to shovel snow *into* them so's the sleds could come through! They cover bridges just as much to keep the *sun* out. A dry bridge will loosen its joints and sag. That's the worst thing a wooden bridge can do."

Sign-painter 45

Airline Pilot

BY THE time Canadian air reaches Ohio its blotter-like dryness will have picked up an abundance of cloud material in the form of water vapor from Lake Michigan and Lake Erie. One might imagine that wetted aid should become heavier; yet it is one of the paradoxes of meteorology that adding moisture to air only makes it lighter. So in the Great Lakes region mornings might be clear and stable yet by noon the warmed air picks up lake moisture and becomes a vast machine of rising currents. Ohio is known to fliers for its afternoon clouding and bumpiness.

A while ago, while researching weather radar, I sat in the co-pilot's seat of an airliner as it skirted Dayton's Wright Field. The clouds of midday had already gathered, and as we pulled up and over them we broke into bright sunlight to rise above a blinding, flat prairie of cumulus clouds. As far as the eye could see, except for a few cumulo-nimbus clouds with heads poking above the white floor, the prairie was endless; it disappeared into every horizon.

Directly in our flight path was one thunderhead that built up even as we looked on. By the time we were a few miles from it, it looked like a volcanic mountain rising out of the sea. If you watched intently you became aware of a slow boiling effect. An anvil top had begun to form, and its white veil streamed ahead of its lofty peak like blown snow.

The pilot nodded in its direction.

"Probably some cool air coming from the northwest underneath that stuff. An anvil top always leans in the direction of the air flow. Notice how that one spreads to the southeast."

By now we were about three miles from the big cloud.

"I hope we're not flying into that," I said.

"Heck, no," the pilot said. "I just thought you'd like to see it up close. It looks like one of those cloudscapes you paint, doesn't it?"

47

"Well, it sure looks mean. I'm completely satisfied with the view from right here."

As the air became turbulent and just before we would have entered the scuddy fringes of the cloud, we banked sharply and began to pass the storm wall to the right. I had read how winds tend to revolve counterclockwise around such storm centers so I presumed we were taking a right course to avoid whatever head-winds that would circle in from the left. All the boiling effect as seen from close range seemed to be boiling *inward* instead of *outward*, substantiating the new theory that a thunderhead does not explode outward but is fed by outside drafts during the time it is building up.

There are "fair-weather cumulus clouds and there are "stormy-looking" cumulus clouds: as a cloud painter I had often wondered what the anatomical difference between the two was. But flying close by a thunderhead it becomes plain, the shapes are quite the same but the *lighting* is different—it is reversed! In fact, if you look at the photographic negative of a fair-weather cloud you will see the picture of an angry storm cloud! In good weather a cloud is all light and shadow produced by the sun, while a storm cloud seems to have a strange light coming from within.

As our radar beam swung into the bowels of the cloud, a big blotch of tinkling light showed up on the screen in the pilot's compartment. As cells of hail bounced the echo back with extra force, they make these spots islands of intense brightness. That's what weather radar does: it picks out the cells of worst turbulence in any storm, so a pilot can pick his way around them just like a slalom skier. My eyes left the scope and I viewed the thunderous wall of cloud outside.

"Did you ever fly into anything like that?" I asked.

The pilot looked at me and beyond me and into some far-away memory.

"I most certainly did. Something even bigger. They come big down in the South Pacific. Funny thing about it though, instead of killing me, it saved my life! Ask me some time and maybe I'll tell you about it."

I reminded him later, and he did tell me about it.

"I was one of three," he told me, "coming back from a scattered scouting mission. There wasn't any sign of action; where the Japs were, at least I didn't know. Flying five miles up, the view was something immense. Down around the equator, where most of the wind goes straight up in the form of thermals, cumulus clouds build up just like castles. It was something pretty spectacular to look at and I forgot all about a war going on.

"Just a few degrees off my flight path there was an afternoon storm building up. In its center was a granddaddy of all thunderheads. At over twenty-five thousand, where I sat, the big cloud still towered above me like the Matterhorn. I'd guess it must have been about sixty thousand feet high. Lightning flickered almost continually inside so it seemed to have a pulsating, sulphury orange glow. It was a real beauty. Back in Airology I had learned how a thing like that can make a mess of a plane so I knew it was something to keep away from. I steered around it and droned alongside like someone in an upper box watching the greatest show in the world.

"Then, all of a sudden, two things happened, both in the same split second. A shadow passed across my canopy and the end of my right wing seemed to explode and disappear. I looked up in time to see the shape and markings of a Jap Zero zoom past my back in a tight loop. I knew he was getting into position for another try.

"The results of my shot-off wing tip didn't show up at once: the ship still flew. I felt it out with the stick; the controls responded in a sloppy sort of way, but I knew combat flying was out of the question. I didn't have a chance against a Zero and I knew I was a dead duck. The only thing I could think of was to head for that storm cloud.

"I guess the yawing and slipping caused by my damaged wing were responsible for his rotten aiming because I was getting near-misses on both sides when I hit the cloud. The next shot would have done the trick: when we were both swallowed by the thunderhead the Zero was just about dead center on my tail.

"You know what a roller coaster does to your insides? Well, once inside of that cloud the battering and slamming around were a lot worse. I remember the wings shuddering and seeing rivets popping. I saw the metal skin on the ship fluttering up and down as if it were rubber. The instruments wouldn't respond fast enough to tell me what position I was in, but I was probably upside down as often as right side up. Then I must have ripped the oxygen hose out of my mask and I must have been thrown up to a higher altitude because everything went black. When I came to, the ship was flying itself. I guess I got clear of the cloud at about ten thousand feet. The plane was a mess, but even with a wing tip gone it was still flying. Grumman made a solid ship. It got me back to the base, and when the mechanics took the wings apart they found most of their internal bracings gone.

"The Zero? I never saw it again. Nobody else did either. But I know damn well what happened. It just never flew out of that cloud. The Zero was a fast and maneuverable little thing; it outflew most of our ships, but it couldn't take the beating that our planes could. Grumman and that thunderhead saved my life."

There are two schools of thought about vertical winds within thunderstorms. One is among certain scientists who have sent balloons and drones up into storms, following their actions by radar. "The updrafts and downdrafts," they claim, "are extremely light, averaging only a few miles an hour. The shock received by fliers (so much publicized in flying accounts) is more from the flier's own speed striking a vertical draft than by the severity of the draft itself."

The other school is among fliers who have been carried aloft while their ship was in a diving position, or smashed into the ground while in climbing attitude.

We can't argue with some of these fliers, for they didn't live through the ordeal. But I do believe in severe thunderstorm drafts in cold-front storms. I believe that the tests made within thunderstorms which showed only slight vertical winds were tests made of thermal thunderstorms (a cumulus cloud overgrown by means of accumulated heat into a cumulo-nimbus) and not fast-moving cold-front thunderheads. Despite what certain scientific tests have shown, then, here is my own version of what happens with a cold-front storm and where the vertical winds are located. Most experienced fliers, I believe, will agree with my diagram.

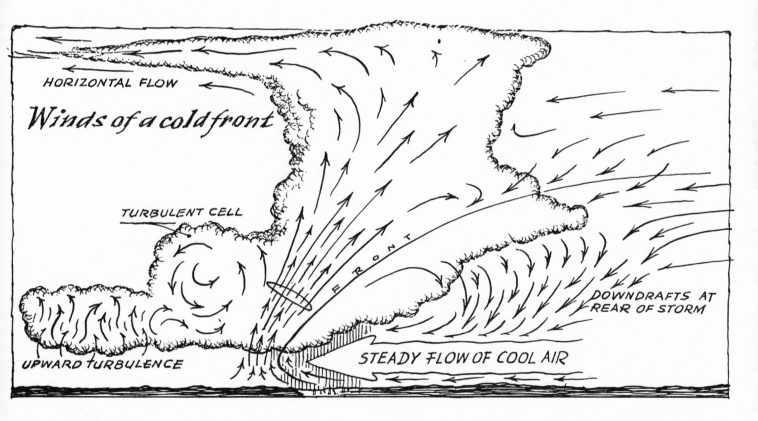

HORIZONTAL FLOW

Winds of a cold front

TURBULENT CELL

FRONT

DOWNDRAFTS AT REAR OF STORM

UPWARD TURBULENCE

STEADY FLOW OF COOL AIR

Birdwatcher

BY THE time cP reaches Pennsylvania it has usually begun its arc to the northeast, heading for the New England coast and then out to sea. The land in Pennsylvania piles up into the Appalachian ridges and when fast, cold-front thunderstorms pass through, they have the habit of skipping from ridge to ridge, saving the valleys from severe downpours. The mountains are entirely composed of parallel ridges that extend across the state in a general northeast-to-southwest direction; and the prevailing westerlies flow across these ridges like wash against a washboard. The long rivers of updrafts that result are a delight to all migrating birds; no matter which way they are heading, it is just a matter of spreading wings against the updraft and following any one of the ridges either northward or southward. Actually, the bird is coasting "downhill" at great speed, but the upward force of wind is so great that a steady altitude may be maintained at express-train forward speed.

Some of Pennsylvania's ridges are known as "hawk ways" because of the constant stream of migrating hawks above them. Bird watchers gather at such places as Hawk Mountain Sanctuary (north of Hamburg, Pennsylvania), and it was there that I first met an unforgettable man named August Raspet. Raspet was a happy combination of naturalist, meteorologist, and sailplane expert.

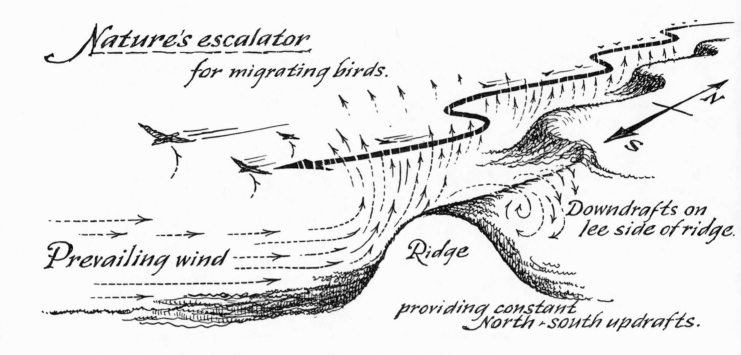

Nature's escalator for migrating birds.

Prevailing wind

Ridge

Downdrafts on lee side of ridge.

providing constant North-south updrafts.

A few bald eagles had already taken the aerial escalator a few weeks before and we were watching the first migration of broad-wing hawks as they sailed overhead in two's and three's at about five-minute intervals. Raspet watched them through binoculars.

"Notice how they follow the ridge," he pointed out, "just like a sailplane would do. I've soared alongside them and I believe they took me for another migrating bird. They turned their heads every now and then to look me over, but they didn't move one inch out of their course unless I threatened to brush wing tips with them. Sometimes they seemed even to doze as they followed the ridge southward."

"It's a wonder nature doesn't send meals aloft to them," I joked, "so they wouldn't have to come down to feed."

But Raspet didn't think I was joking.

"That's just about what happens," he said. "There's a lot of aerial plankton up there that we don't see but the birds do. Some of the stuff is big enough to see—like spiders. I've seen spiders so thick at two thousand feet that they looked like snow. When the sun shone on their gossamer webs it looked like angel hair on a Christmas tree."

I thought at first that Raspet was pulling my leg. But his scientific mind was always so busy that it had little time for humor; his words were always chosen and precise, always true. Even from a short conversation with him, I realized later on, cascaded an unbelievable pool of facts which he himself had discovered or researched.

"You've seen gossamer—those webs that sparkle with dew during late summer? Well, they weren't spun by local spiders as many people might think: they fell from the sky! They probably come from hundreds of miles away. They are the webs that spiders fly or 'balloon' with. But you're a weatherman—you probably know all about that."

I assured him that I didn't.

"Well," he continued, "I found that in autumn, when certain spiders are hatched, the babies spin webs as an outlet for their energy. When exposed to even a puff of wind, a young spider automatically throws out jets of silken web just as a child instinctively throws its arms and legs about as a human reaction.

"Sometimes the spider will hang from one long web and then let out another web that flows out farther in the wind. Then, when the first web or 'mooring' breaks, the spider is airborne and the ballooning begins. A balloon trip might take one or two weeks and the distances covered are amazing. Ships five hundred miles at sea have been showered with spiders during early Indian summer."

"Why Indian summer?" I asked.

"Perhaps it coincides with bird migration as you suggested before," he said. "Anyway, during that time there is calmer ground air and greater updrafts and drier atmosphere. It's just better

"How a spider goes "ballooning"....

Wind →

1. Hanging by web (A), - - - - - - - - it puts out another web (B)

2. When web (B) is long and pulls hard enough, web (A) breaks ...and the spider is airborne

3. Warm air thermals lift the spider and its web "wings" into jet-type air streams

4. When ready to descend, it pulls its webs in, winding them into a ball ...and lands

ballooning weather for spiders. The spiders don't spin out their gossamer jets in damp air; they wait for the passage of a dry air mass.

"As a matter of fact, the word gossamer *means* Indian summer. What Americans call Indian summer was once called Goose summer (gos-somer in early English). Here we place Indian summer as the first warm spell after the first frost; in England they used to watch for the first Goose summer webs.

"Funny thing about the spiders' ballooning, though, is how they control flight just like a real balloon pilot. The might travel for two weeks and cover a thousand miles. But when they want to come down, or when a storm approaches, they gather in their flight webs and roll them up into a neat ball until they begin to lose altitude. If they fall too fast, however, they control their fall by casting out more web."

Raspet's name will long be remembered in the annals of science; but I shall recall him best when he looked at the sky and became a philosopher.

7 Farmer

THE SIMPLE vagaries of the wind were at one time a subject of agricultural study; each crop was planted windwise, one growth sheltering another until a final tree windbreak protected all the lesser plants. Water was pumped from the ground by windmill and the wind shelled corn, ground mash, sawed wood, churned butter, made paint from linseed oil, turned grindstones, chopped oats, made cider, and did a hundred other farm chores. In the beginning there were twice as many windmills as watermills, and when the waterwheels were frozen to a standstill until late spring, the windmills continued to function as America's industrial promise.

Sailors once made their sightings by the hundreds of windmill towers along the Atlantic coast; smaller portable mills pumped seawater into shallow evaporation vats to produce salt. The New York City ferry was at one time required to stop services "when the windmill [on the Battery or tip of Manhattan] hath taken in or lowered its sails because of turbulent winds, consequent of storm or otherwise." Evidently the windmill on the Battery was our first weather bureau. Weather cycles have come and gone, with some remarkable examples of warmth, coldness, wetness, and drought; yet throughout the ages the wind averages have been almost constant.

Twenty-five years ago I had the audacity to make a living by criticizing professional meteorologists. Not all meteorologists, but just a certain few. At that time, the past decade of winters had been exceedingly mild and a few weathermen were working overtime in print, telling how the American climate was changing. "Bad winters," they wrote, "are a thing of the past. It is only a matter of a few centuries before the icecap will melt to flood all cities along the Atlantic Coast by some fifty feet of water!" It made spectacular copy, with illustrations of New York's skyscrapers sticking out of the sea.

59

Page from a weather diary, 1861

And that's where I came in.

Popular Science magazine asked me to illustrate one of these changing climate stories, and I refused.

"No," I said, "I'll not illustrate what I believe to be untrue; particularly when I also write about the weather myself. I don't think the climate is changing so drastically and I believe we are merely going through a climate cycle."

"Well, then," said the editor, "just don't sign your name to the illustration, and stop being a prima donna. Tell you what I'll do. You do the illustration and we'll add a squib telling how Eric Sloane disagrees with the story and in the next issue you can write a rebuttal." I accepted that offer.

The first article that I submitted was titled "Warm Winters Are Just a Cycle." The second was to *Mechanix Illustrated* titled "Wait Ten Years—Cold Winters Will Be Back!" Other publications picked up the idea and for a while I badgered the weather writers to the point of becoming a nuisance.

As I write these lines (twenty-five years later) for this book it is April the tenth. The temperature is 24 degrees F. and a fifty-mile wind is ruffling the New England landscape into an icy scene. It has been snowing since dawn and there is a six-inch accumulation of fresh snow. Changing climate, indeed!

One of my research interests has been the collecting of ancient almanacs and farm diaries, noticing, particularly, the remarks that pertain to weather and the sky. The findings that crop up are always quaint and precious but often they are no less than astounding. For example, I found from one farm diary that the weather over a hundred years ago (1861) was identical to that of 1970 (up until April). The particular diary was kept as all farmers did then, giving wind direction, state of the sky, and pertinent

translation

remarks. Temperatures were taken at sunrise, noon, sunset, and 10 P.M., and extremes for each month were calculated at the end of the page. The name of the farmer is unknown, but this diary was found in a barn near Franklin Lakes, New Jersey (about twenty miles from New York).

Knowing how the early farmers used weather information as a farm tool, and how observant these people were of the sky, I feel that reproducing a sample page from this farm weather diary might be in place. (My wife Ruth deciphered the more difficult writing, and her translation appears on the page opposite.)

I wish the Weather Bureau might use the descriptive weather language that the old-timers used, for they did tell the weather story so well. *A Sour Day* appears often, as does *sloppy underfoot, angry sky, dull and damp, beautiful day, blustery, chilly, showery and uncertain, abortive attempt at rain,* and *quiet sky.*

The entry under March 26 is reminiscent of our present flying-saucer age. I wonder what the "nine strange lights" were. Certainly nothing to do with Russia. Notice how this plain farmer found time to observe the birds, the frogs, the aurora borealis, and all the panorama of sky. People really enjoyed the sky to its fullest in those days, and felt called upon to record it. I guess the idea of a weather diary today would be regarded as a childish waste of time.

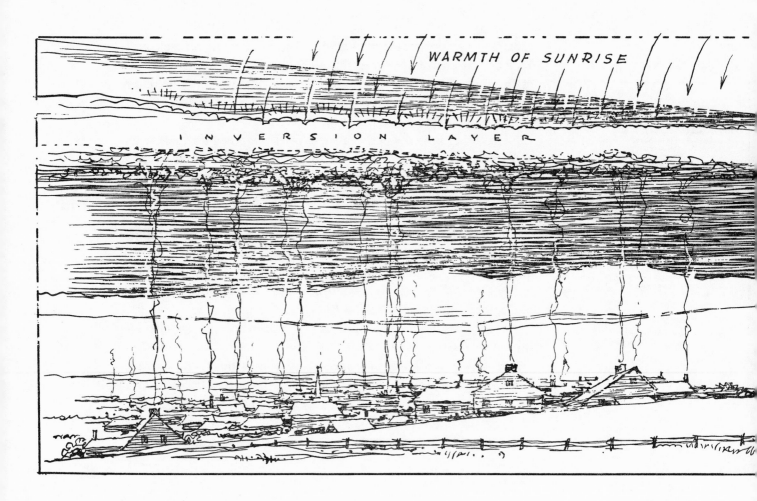

Doorman

One of the strangest truths of meteorology is that when you add water to air it becomes lighter. Invisible air seems so negative and water seems so positive in its dead weight that the idea of moist air rising like a balloon over dry air seems improbable. Add the fact that air cools as it rises from the earth and you begin to realize what a symphony of vertical movements intermix with dry or wet, warm or cold horizontal winds. If different qualities of air had different colors, the sky would look like the writhing flow of colored lights in those old-fashioned jukeboxes, never quiet, always mixing. But that is good; when air becomes quiet, when its constant dance is stilled, life begins to cease. When an inversion in the natural mechanics of weather happens, people begin to cease being—slowly perhaps, with some coughing and slowing of the pulse, but if it were not for a cold air mass to sweep away the polluted sky mechanism and bring newly mixed clean air, the process of dying would continue.

63

If you have ever motored into the country on a windless, cold early morning, you will have seen a simplified diagram of aerial inversion; smoke of early breakfast-time fires rises from chimneys, moving upward in the natural way of warm, wet air. But just about a thousand feet up, where the first rays of the sun have already hit, the air has been too suddenly warmed. There, like a ceiling, is an unnatural layer of warm air; and the smoke, halted completely by the inverse mechanics, gathers into a flat stratus inversion layer. Every now and then (and more often as time goes on) this phenomenon occurs on a grand scale when a persistent warm air mass has lingered too long and collected the garbage of big-city pollution. I've seen such an inversion layer over New York, when smog warnings were announced and the only hope seemed to be the visit of our life-saving continental polar air-mass broom.

When cP descends over New York City, many things happen. City people who seldom look upward take notice of the little whirlpools of dust that revolve in alleys between apartment houses and in the sunken "areaways" of brownstone houses. Full-size whirlwinds occur in the open streets.

Air laden with dust and carbon particles begins to balloon upward through the cooler air flow, carrying tiny trash and newspaper shreds to amazing heights. Downtown, hundreds of feet above the street, bits of paper ride the warm drafts that squeeze through the new air and visit from building to building. Every now and then a particularly strong thermal will lift as much as twenty pounds of aerial trash above the rooftops and send it into the seabound air stream. Air pilots have seen full sheets of newspaper floating serenely far out over the Atlantic. cP is indeed the big city air-conditioner. The only one. One pilot recognized a sheet of the *New York Daily News* over Bermuda.

When the planes let down their landing gears and lose altitude over Manhattan as they approach La Guardia Airport, they are battered by jarring blasts of thermal updraft. These blobs of heat ascending from the streets burble upward like bubbles in champagne; on a hot summer's day, just after a cold air mass has

Look at the Sky . . .
and tell the Weather 64

come through, a light plane can easily gain a thousand feet just by hitting these continuous bumps over Manhattan. A large plane can idle its engines and coast without losing altitude for the whole length of the island.

In clear, cool air *immediately after* a cold front has passed, at only two thousand you can at the same time see the Statue of Liberty and the roller coasters of Coney Island. Westward you can pick out Newark and see far into the Ramapo Mountains of New Jersey. City smoke that ordinarily gathers over Manhattan in fog-like sheets and makes visibility poor suddenly becomes confined in the new cool air: columns of factory smoke lean toward the southeast looking as if they were bent appendages of the chimneys themselves. There is a sense of global movement as the vast sea of cold air moves steadily over the city like an invisible glacier.

Down below in the streets there is a strange sense of continuous movement. Traffic moves nicely in high-pressure weather, like endless chains in a machine: there is none of the unevenness or snarls that seem to occur mostly during the overcast of low-pressure weather. People walk briskly in the dense, clear air because they feel better. It's nothing new. A thousand years ago King Alfred observed it when he wrote: "So it falls that men are with fine weather happier far"; two centuries ago Benjamin Franklin said: "Do business with men when the wind is from the northwest." Today there are people in Wall Street who buy and sell stocks according to the movement of the barometer. They sell during high pressure when cP comes through, and they buy a few hours after the barometer goes down!

Mr. Terwilliger was one of my favorite New York weather experts. He was a doorman at the Hotel Biltmore, so he observed the comings and goings of many people. "You know," he told me, "that barometer you gave me works like a charm. When the pressure goes up, people tip like mad. When the pressure goes down, they keep their hands in their pockets."

I knew Terwilliger for a long time. I first met him while walking along an abandoned road in Long Island. He was burning autumn leaves and his car was parked nearby: I waved a hello. "Do you work here?" I asked him.

"No," he replied. "I'm a doorman at the Hotel Biltmore in New York. But I did work on that estate yonder a long while ago. I miss the open sky and I've never forgotten the good smell of burning autumn leaves. So every year I drive out here just to burn a few leaves and breathe in the perfume. It does my soul good and it's better for me than any vacation I can think of."

Terwilliger was also expert on predicting weather by observing the color of one patch of sky.

"That rectangle of sky on Forty-third Street outside the Biltmore might not seem to have much color to you," he told me, "but when it's been all the sky you've had to look at day after day for a quarter of a century, you get to know it pretty well. It's like seeing an old friend; if he's slightly flushed or if he's a little pale, you notice it right away, don't you? Well, my little spot of sky is an old friend; I can tell his complexion where I guess most people wouldn't notice it.

"It's a funny thing about New York: I think the dust in the air reflects the city's color. People say that the sky in New York is as colorful as anywhere else in the world. One lady stopping at the hotel just came in from Venice. She says the sunset in New York beats anything she's ever seen in Italy.

"In the summer the sun sets right over the end of West Forty-third Street stretching the width of the street; not many people seem to notice it, but it sure makes my day worth while."

I liked Terwilliger!

One day I stopped to chat with him, and I suggested in good humor that he start a little weather service of his own. So many people greeted him on their way out with a "What's the weather going to be?"

"You'd be surprised," he said, "how many people do ask me just that. The weather means quite a lot to some New Yorkers. See that fellow I just opened the door for? That's Douglas Leigh —the fellow who makes the big signs on Broadway. One winter

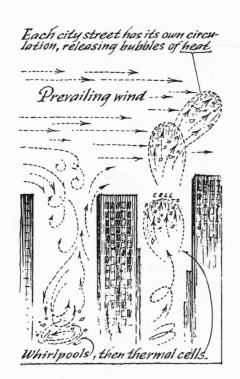

Each city street has its own circulation, releasing bubbles of heat.

Prevailing wind

CELL

Whirlpools, then thermal cells.

he used about ten thousand gallons of anti-freeze in that Times Square Pepsi-Cola waterfall sign. Every time it freezes or hails or even rains he loses a lot of money on tens of thousands of cracked light bulbs. You know, I can just about tell when bad weather's on its way by the expression on his face."

A man stepped out of the hotel and glanced at the sky.

"What's it going to do, Terwilliger?" It was more in the tone of a statement than a question.

"I'd go back for a topcoat Mr. Martin," said Terwilliger. "It's going to be cold tonight." The man turned and went back inside.

Terwilliger winked at me.

"See what I mean?"

Drover

CONNECTICUT is a tiny state, yet the advance of cP air is always felt inland a few hours there before it reaches the coast line. The difference in temperature between Connecticut's inland hills and the shore is often as much as thirty degrees.

Ephram Tuck lifted the window shade and looked out into the Berkshire night. Stars gleamed in a steel-black sky, gyrating like grotesque lights in the bubbles of old hand-made glass panes.

"Clear as a bell out there," he said, as if he were speaking to someone other than himself.

A dog near the iron stove lifted his head from folded forepaws and looked at the old man.

"Best we got to bed," said Ephram, now addressing the dog. "We might as well get an early start. Loading twenty-four crates of turkeys will take up a fair spell of the morning."

Ephram turned the oil lamp down, nearly out. But after a

hesitant thought he turned the wick up again. He then spread the prongs of his spectacle frames apart, adjusted them to his head, and began searching through a tall stack of farm papers. From somewhere near the bottom he picked out a worn almanac and thumbed through its pages until the proper date came to view.

"Tuesday," he read aloud. "Fair skies and cool winds. Squally days are coming soon. Haul your goods in First Gibbous Moon. Best time for selling."

After this quotation there were thirteen pencil marks, each one indicating a trip made to town on that day during the past years. Ephram picked up a stub of pencil, touched it to his lips, and with the wet pencil added a fourteenth mark.

"Best day for selling," he repeated.

Like his father before him and his father's father, Ephram made very few moves about the Connecticut countryside without first consulting his almanacs. If one almanac said nothing about the day in question, another one from the dusty stack probably would. And if there were no hints at all to be found, the whole trip would be put off until some more favorable day, one suggested by the almanac.

Ephram learned his weather knowledge and trust in almanacs from Grandfather Tuck whose business of droving depended on such lore. But the success of a drove depended upon a great many other things, too.

Drover Tuck was only ten years old when he was allowed to go as apprentice on his first turkey drive, back in the days when all livestock was "droved" or walked to market. The story of that trip had been handed down to Ephram, who enjoyed repeating it to whoever might listen. He usually told the story when someone criticized his faith in the almanacs or whenever the subject of weather came up.

"Let me tell you," Ephram would start, "about the year without a summer."

What Ephram told them was hard to believe, yet history does

substantiate the facts. There actually was such a year when New England had so cold a summer that it became known as "1816— the summerless year." Men worked in the fields with mittens on during June the seventh, and at the end of that day it snowed in upper New England. On the Fourth of July, in Woodbury, Connecticut, there was a celebration in the village green and everyone wore overcoats. Men pitched quoits with fur gloves on to keep the iron rings from freezing to their fingers. According to reliable records somewhere in the middle states snow was seen every day during every month of the *year*.

Ephram will show you a tattered copy of the Danville *North Star* dated June 15, 1816. "On the night of June 6th," it reads, "water froze an inch thick, and on the night of the 7th and morning of the 8th a kind of sleet or exceedingly cold snow fell, attended by a high wind, and measured in places where it drifted 18 to 20 inches in depth."

"Well, sir," Ephram would relate as if he were there at the time, "only half of the corn ripened that year. The turkeys were so skinny from lack of feed that they just barely made the drive."

Most drives consisted of cattle or sheep with a few fowl, but about a month before Thanksgiving many drives of nothing but turkeys started on New England roads, headed for Boston. Some folks say that the big droves were one of the reasons they covered the old wooden bridges. It made them look like houses: driven fowl that might break out of line and go down into the water were more apt to herd peaceably through a covered bridge and cross it as if they were going through a barn.

Drover Tuck always managed one such drive from Woodbury to Boston, picking up flocks of turkeys along the way. The distance was about two hundred miles, and, like average turkey drives, they progressed about ten miles a day. In later years there were almost unbelievably big turkey drives, some going all the way from middle Vermont into Boston, with ten to fifteen thousand birds and a drover force of nearly a hundred people. Such drives needed wagon trains for camping equipment and several wagons just for feed. But Drover Tuck's Woodbury drive of 1816 was one of the early ones; it probably had no more than two or three thousand birds. Because of the shortage of feed from the bad summer that year, there was only one small wagonload of grain, and that gave out long before Boston was reached. It was difficult to keep the drove on the road.

"The birds were so starved," the story goes, "that they attacked every grain field along the way. Farmers had to beat them away with sticks, and Grandfather Tuck got sued for broken apple trees where the turkeys roosted at night and ate the fruit right off the limbs. The turkeys did more foraging along the roadside than they did traveling, and it got so that soon three miles a day was pretty good.

"After awhile the ground got frozen and the turkeys couldn't walk on the hard road so Grandfather Tuck painted their feet with thick tar. That protected their feet and it brought them back to the road. When they got close to Boston, where the sea air is warm and salty, things got better, but even so, the drove got to market almost a month late.

"Funny thing about the drive though," says Ephram, "is that Grandfather Tuck knew he'd lost a lot of turkeys along the way. Farmers shot some of them for breaking their orchard trees, and foxes hungered by the cold summer attacked the drove while it rested at night, and ate a lot of them. But when they got counted at the market place there were sixty more turkeys than when they started out! Grandfather Tuck said they must have been wild turkeys driven down from the hills by hunger and joined up with the drove."

"And what about the almanac," you might ask Ephram, "didn't it predict that cold summer?"

To answer such a question he will pull out a special almanac, kept hidden in a cigar box. The year printed on the old paper cover is 1816, the very year of the big cold spell. Written across the top in faded mulberry juice ink is the name of Drover Tuck himself.

"Read what it says here," Ephram will say. "I can't read what that fine print says without my glasses."

He could read it all right, and he even knows it by heart; but having you read it aloud seems more emphatic to Ephram, as if he has won a point.

"June 25th," it reads, "beginning of clear and cold summer."

"Better predicting than they do nowadays, isn't it?" Ephram will say. "The insurance company meteorologist from Hartford came up here one day and I showed it to him. Didn't have much to say about it, though. Doesn't believe in almanacs."

Actually the insurance company meteorologist does believe in almanacs. He knows that they were the best that people could do in those days and that they did an extraordinary job. He was amused at the entry for June 25, 1816, for it was really meant to read: "Beginning of summer—*clear and cold*," and the "*clear and cold*," which was marginal and in italic, referred to just that one day which was the beginning of summer.

"But if Ephram enjoys it so," he says, "I'll not be the one to tell him different. About that 'first gibbous moon' being 'best time for selling,' sure that was true a century ago, and there was nothing mysterious at all about it. In the early days it often took a man a day or maybe two or three to get to the nearest town to sell; the farmer who traveled both day and night needed plenty of moonlight for such a trip. The early gibbous moon which is just before a full moon gives the longest-lasting and greatest amount of moonlight to travel by. It was that simple. Everything was done by the moon in those days, and people didn't think there was anything mystic attached to it as we think they did.

"Few realize how many things were done by moonlight and one reason is that our eyesight has deteriorated within the last century or two because of a lessening of proper vitamins in daily diet. The night vision of a man two centuries ago seems to have been remarkable. Roofing, haying and other chores, which would have been unbearably hot in midsummer, were often done at night. The fact that there used to be night hunting for raccoon and fox is well known but few have thought about the absence of electric torches in those days.

"The moon was a lantern, calendar, governor of tides, a thing to set your clock by, and a hundred other tools that a farmer could make use of. Nowadays even though we're in the 'space age' you can ask an average American where the moon sets and rises or what its path is through the sky, and he won't be able to tell you without guessing. The old-timers were a lot more space con-

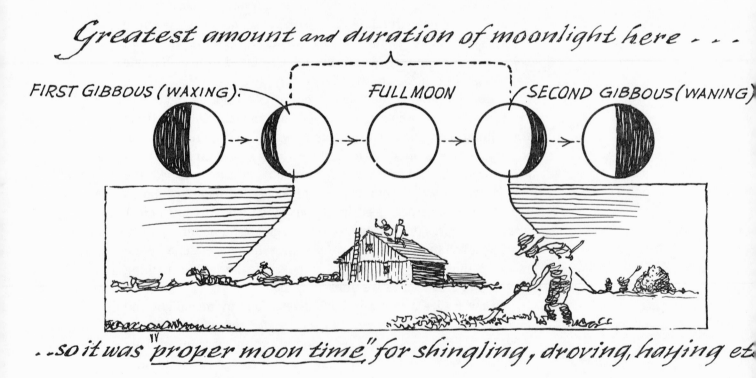

Greatest amount and duration of moonlight here . . .

FIRST GIBBOUS (WAXING). FULL MOON (SECOND GIBBOUS (WANING)

. . so it was "proper moon time" for shingling, droving, haying et

scious and weatherwise than is the average person today. Yet we so often seem to enjoy thinking that their faith in the planets and seasons and nature lore was just a lot of quaint superstition.

"But if old Ephram likes to think there is something special and mysterious about the moon and his almanacs, God bless him. There's too little notice of the skies nowadays, until someone wants to criticize us weather people."

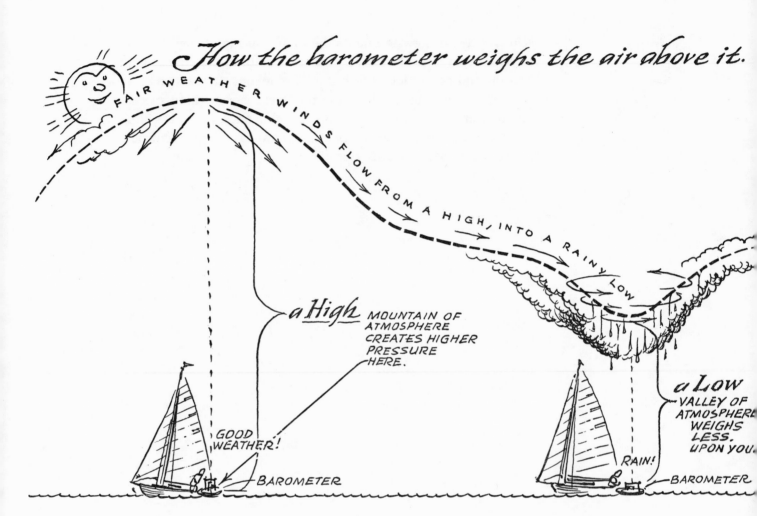

How the barometer weighs the air above it.

FAIR WEATHER WINDS FLOW FROM A HIGH, INTO A RAINY LOW

a High MOUNTAIN OF ATMOSPHERE CREATES HIGHER PRESSURE HERE.

GOOD WEATHER!

BAROMETER

a Low VALLEY OF ATMOSPHERE WEIGHS LESS. UPON YOU.

RAIN!

BAROMETER

Sailor

cP HAS been said to rule New England's weather. I know this because I said it myself. *Field and Stream* magazine had asked me to start doing a weather article for each issue that featured some certain hunting or fishing area. My first assignment was East Africa, my second was Venezuela, and so on, to remote spots that I'd never even heard of; but with a little research and a few hints from the airline travel folders, I always came up with an efficient weather and climate analysis. That is, until my assignment was *New England*. There, in the very place in which I lived, I found the greatest difficulty in writing about my own weather. If you'd ask a New Englander what place has a climate ranging from 50 degrees F. below to 100 degrees F. above, he'd rarely think of his own countryside. It was such a tough assignment that I almost gave up my *Field and Stream* job.

New England is a tightrope where the weather usually balances between warm maritime air and the periodic flows of cold continental air from the northwest. So if ever there was a place where amateur folklore weather prophets do their best work, I might suggest New England. The tightrope between the two air masses often waves and writhes, causing sunny weather in one spot while rain is only a mile or two away. You can't show that sort of thing on a weather map. A New England weather prophet just has to know his sky and wind and remember by past experiences what follows which sky phenomena.

Nowadays when you buy a barometer it is usually decorated and sold as a marine device; in fact, they are sold as "ship's barometers." Yet the barometer is one of the poorest of weather prophets, and the old-time sailor seldom sailed by its readings.

77

I've seen it rain hard during a barometric high, and I've seen fine sailing weather during a low. The trouble is that the barometer, like a clock, tells you only what the reading is at the moment you read it. What you really need to know is whether the pressure has been rising, falling, or steady and whether the change has been erratic, rapid, or slow. To know this, you'd have to make hourly records; or you could use a barograph, which records the pressures minute by minute and hour by hour on a graph paper. The barometer is nothing but a weighing machine (like a bathroom scales), but it weighs the valleys and mountains of air as they flow overhead. The trick is to detect an oncoming valley of bad weather or the approach of a mountain of good weather. Reading a barometer indication just at a given moment is rather like trying to tell time with a stopped clock.

Westy Lyons is my idea of an expert at folklore weather predictions. Duxbury is a big harbor and a gaff-rigged catboat like Westy's needed every bit of wind wisdom a sailing man could muster, to navigate.

"I don't go along with those old-time goose-quill and caterpillar predictions," he told me. "My granny used to try never to step on an ant because 'it meant rain.' Nonsense! There's so much tommyrot folklore going around that most folks just don't take stock in *any* of it. Yet there's a lot of true folklore.

"After watching the weather for over half a century and making note of what happens in and around the harbor, I can find a lot more information in the sky than I can in those complicated Boston weather maps, folklore or not.

"You take any early morning, before a fellow wants to sail, and the wind hasn't come up as yet. Most folks don't know just what to expect. But you just seek out a high cloud and determine which way she's a-blowin'; that's the wind a fellow can expect later on in the day." (Author's note: this is usually true, because winds do tend to lower. Whatever wind is high above any calm area, that wind usually lowers to earth level in time.)

"Most city folk look out over the water, and if it's clear and a distant point looms out distinct-like to the eye, they say: 'That's a sign of good weather.' Yet any real sailing man knows it's just a sign of rain." (Author's note: in good weather, salt water evaporates fast and this causes a haze above the distant level, making low-level visibility poor. But unstable air mixes away this salt haze and that makes distant points "loom" closer. Expect rain on the following day.)

"Some yachting folk from Boston like to sail within sight of

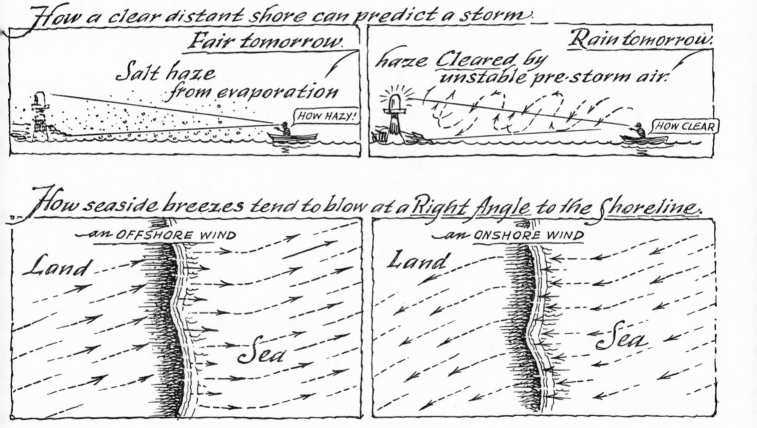

land," says Westy, "and they expect the wind to flow the same way near the shore as it does a mile or so out. They don't know that wind always favors the shore at right angles." (Author's note: this is also true. Wind, whether off shore or on shore, if blowing at an angle to the shore it always tends to shift and head directly into or out from the straight line of shore.)

"Folks always say how sailing men watch the sky for 'mare's-tails' and 'mackerel skies' and then duck for harbor. Well, it just isn't true. A wisp of mare's-tail cloud is just as healthy a sailin' sign as you'd want, and a patch of high mackerel sky doesn't mean much one way or the other either. What you want to watch

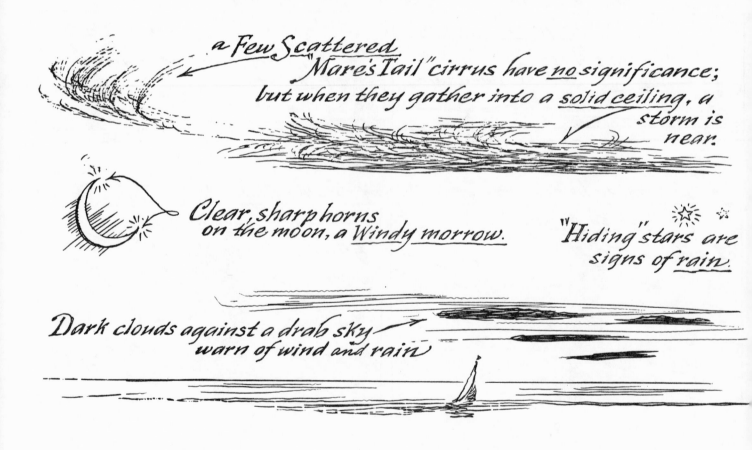

a Few Scattered "Mare's Tail" cirrus have _no significance_; but when they gather into a _solid ceiling_, a storm is near.

Clear, sharp horns on the moon, a _Windy morrow_.

"Hiding" stars are signs of _rain_.

Dark clouds against a drab sky warn of wind and rain

out for on a day at sea are those low, long, flat, dark clouds. They mean a storm is close by.

"Some city folks will look toward an east wind and expect the storm to come from the east. Any old-timer knows that the wind blows like a pinwheel. If you want to locate any storm, just face the wind and point out with your right hand. You'll be pointing into the center of the 'pinwheel,' at the nearest storm. You can follow the eye of a hurricane that way, too."

Folklore expert? Scientist? Westy is both. For the more you look into folklore and weather science, the closer are the two.

Author

BY THE time cP reaches upper New England its strength has often waned considerably; it is then that it sets an irregular course out over the North Atlantic. Weathermen like to think of cP as a bubble of cold air that swings from the end of a pendulum hinged somewhere in Newfoundland. The swinging mass that started in Canada and dipped southward and eastward usually flies clear of its "pendulum" and floats out to sea somewhere near Maine.

The old saltbox farmhouse that I had been remodeling was high up on a Maine mountain where it was the greatest of pleasures for me to watch the almost constant parade of clouds that came in from the northwest. One morning I looked into the sky and I breathed in quantities of particularly refreshing air. It was easy to recognize as cP atmosphere. With an unnoticed shower during the night, cP had moved up from Vermont, lifted mountain clouds from the New Hampshire high places, swept night fogs from along the Maine coast, and finally cleared the morning sky over northern Maine. The blue sky overhead was crisp and steely, and there were the many telltale puffs of white cumulus that usually fly in the wake of dry, cold, northwest air.

It was something special to be alive on such a morning. As I stood in the doorway enjoying it all, Harley, the handy man, came chugging up the driveway in his Model-A truck which came to a steaming halt before me. He swung his overalled legs out of the space where there was once a door, and stepped down limberly.

"Fine morning," he said. "Things a bit damp, though. A mite too damp for *vahnishing*." Harley never pronounced varnish with an r; he gave it a good flat New England accent. To him it was *vahnish*.

"Harley," I said, "I want to get the varnishing through with. Let's do it today! Never mind the dampness. The day looks good to me."

83   When I'd bought the old place "as is and with all furnish-

ings," one of its most prized contents was found in the attic—a shiny five-gallon can marked SPAR VARNISH. At first I thought it might be old and spoiled, antique, like everything else in the place. But the can looked new, and when I opened it the liquid poured forth clear and golden just as good fresh varnish should. So I instructed Harley to scrape the upper floors of the old house, and I slated the five-gallon can for his finishing them off. What luck, I thought!

"Still think it's a mite damp for vahnishing," insisted Harley. "According to my calculations we should have a brisk shower 'long about four o'clock. Mite damp for pain-tin', I'd say."

"Some time, Harley," I said, "I'll tell you all about weather. You see those cumulus clouds overhead?"

"You mean them white clouds yonder?"

"Yes, I mean them white clouds yonder! They mean fair weather. They happen only after a cold air mass has swept through; furthermore, they mean that it won't rain for at least a day or two. What makes you think it will rain at four o'clock, anyway?"

"Looked at the moon last night," drawled Harley, "and it had fuzzy horns. Not sharp and clear like they're supposed to be. Never knew that sign to fail this time of the year. Father used to tell us forget the hayin' when there was fuzzy horns on the moon. Means a rain the next day 'long about four in the afternoon. Ground didn't have no dew on it last night, either, so I'm right certain about it."

"O.K., Fuzzy Horns," I laughed. "But I'll take the United States Weather Bureau's word for it and they say *clear*. Remember, Harley, I've written three books about weather! I say it *won't* rain. So be a good fellow. You'll find the brushes up in the attic alongside that five-gallon varnish can. See you later! I'm going to do some writing." Harley shuffled off toward the attic.

By early afternoon cP had drifted out to sea. The flow of cold air weakened by its long trip and the mixing of coastal sea air had allowed the high cumulus puffs to lower into ragged gray swatches, and the clearness of the morning had quickly deteriorated into a sultry afternoon. cP had swung out to sea leaving the land in an uncertain state of weather. Almost on the dot of four there was a single clap of thunder and rain began to fall on the tin roof of the outhouse. Harley thumped downstairs and called from the hallway.

"You there, Mr. Sloane?"

"O.K., Fuzzy Horns, you win! The joke is on me. I don't know how you do it. I think you should work for the Weather Bureau!"

"Oh, *that!*" he said. "Didn't come down to talk about that 'tall. It's about the *vahnish*. Guess the joke is on me this time. After all, I've lived up here in the sugar country for long enough to've known. Yes, siree, the joke is sure on me."

"What the devil," said I, "are you talking about?"

"Why, about the *vahnish*. 'Twasn't vahnish 'tall! Folks up here buy their containers wholesale from surplus factory stocks t' save a penny or two. Now you take me, I buy surplus olive-oil cans. Others buy varnish cans, like that one up in the attic. Pity I used so much, for it was right fine flavorful syrup."

"You mean you painted the floor with *maple syrup?*" I groaned.

"Yep," he said. "Most of one room and clear out into the hall. *Looks* like vahnish. *Shines* like vahnish. *Doesn't smell like vahnish,* though. The joke is sure on me!"

Before night had fallen Harley had wiped the maple syrup from the newly scraped floor and washed it down with vinegar and soda.

"Scarce a day goes by I don't reap some kind of lesson," he said before he left, "but this is one I don't suspect I can talk too much about. Folks would never stop pokin' fun at me. I'd be obliged, Mr. Sloane, if you'd kind of forget about it."

I'd learned a lesson, too—one about the sky. I'd learned that by the time cP reaches Maine its wallop is sometimes gone; that by then it has begun its swing off the end of its "global pendu-

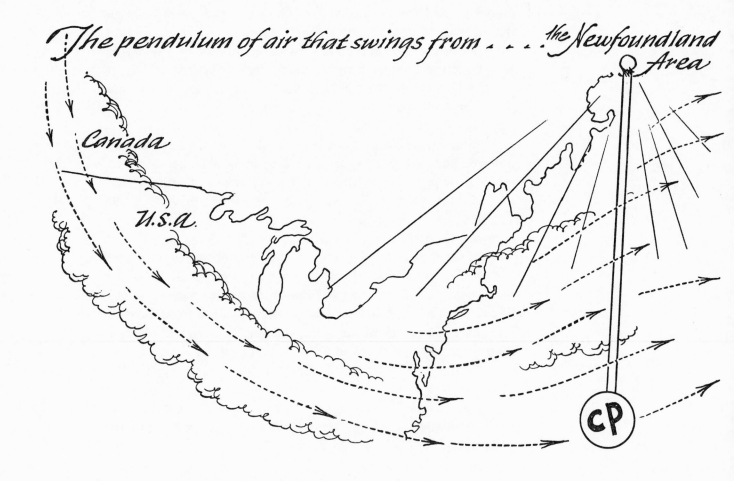

The pendulum of air that swings from . . . . the Newfoundland Area

Canada

U.S.A.

CP

lum" to float out over the Atlantic. I learned that as at many other places, when you are Down East, you can't afford to overlook local lore; that local lore is an accumulation of knowledge from the things that people have heard and seen.

When I first exclaimed that the sky was created for pure beholding, my scientific leanings did cause me to cringe a bit. I sounded overpoetic and even trite to myself. Yet, when I think of it, the sights and sounds of the countryside can be no accident. Just as sure as the eye is designed for seeing, it seems logical that there must be things designed to be seen.

In nature there are all sorts of warning signals designed to be seen (or, in the case of camouflage, designed *not* to be seen). But I think that nature didn't stop just at warning signals: I am convinced that the sky and its clouds are things designed for man's information and spiritual contentment. I am certain that the sky was designed to be seen by man.

The trip of one air mass through the United States was done. Its contribution to the lives and thoughts of many people was finished. Tomorrow a warm air mass might flow in from the sea carrying with it the flavor of salt and the feeling of wetness. But some cP child is always being born up in distant Mackenzie Territory, perhaps packing up and readying to leave this very minute, heading my way. I'll wait and see. And look at the sky.

AFTERWORD

THE YEAR 1970 marks the centennial of the Weather Bureau. It began in the Army Signal Corps in 1870 and today is a branch of the Environmental Science Services Administration. Forecasting is a blend of old and new sciences, but the new sciences are almost entirely those of communication; the basic instruments are still such as those Benjamin Franklin knew. Balloons tracked by radar, photos taken from space, three- and twelve-hour reports from thousands of sources, electronic information fed to computers—all this adds up to faster, more accurate, and more informative communication. But to a large extent the forecast is still the result of past experience and what seems to be developing. That's the same theory used at the racetrack.

Let me be the last to belittle the Weather Bureau. If you really want to know what the weather is going to be tomorrow, look to the Weather Bureau as you'd go to a doctor when you are ailing. But there are still important first-aid rules and health hints to keep you well; and there are still weather rules and lore that sometimes prove as good as or better than the "weather doctor's" report. At least, such lore adds to your knowledge and makes living in God's world a bit more exciting.

If you want to tell the weather, your first observation should be of the wind direction. In the United States the prevailing wind (which is the wind of fair weather) is westerly; it is often northwesterly during the winter and southwesterly during the summer. By keeping a written record, you can learn in a month or so what weather each wind brings in your location. Your prime weather instrument, then, would be a good, easy-swinging wind vane. A "veering" wind (one changing from prevailing to nonprevailing) will bring stormy skies; a "backing" wind (one changing from nonprevailing to prevailing) will bring clearing skies. As previously mentioned, if you face the wind and point to your right, you will always be pointing to the nearest low-pressure center or storm area.

Secondly, the sky and its clouds will give the folklore weather prophet an indication of what is to be. Since a warm air mass has stratus-type clouds (straight, ceiling-like, and flat), you can often look out the window and recognize a warm air mass surrounding you. And since cumulus clouds (accumulated and lumpy) are associated with a cold air mass, you can tell when such a mass surrounds you or is approaching. The higher and puffier the cumulus, the drier and longer-lasting good weather will be. A confused sky of several heights and types of clouds indicates that confused weather of changing winds and short showers is on the way. Frequently there will be large, dark cumulus clouds sailing from the west, looking like an oncoming storm, but as long as the winds are westerly and the clouds are high (fair sign) no rain will result.

As is shown on the fold-out chart, a halo of the sun or moon is the result of the light shining through high cirro-stratus ice clouds. A flashlight shining through a cake of ice would produce a halo too. Usually (more especially in summer than in winter) a halo shows cirro-stratus clouds that are the uppermost head of an oncoming warm front and so indicates that a period of long, slow rain is on the way.

A warm front can be quite cold, and a cold front can be warmish; the idea is simply that the oncoming new air mass is warmer or colder than the air it replaces. Night air becoming even slightly colder after 9 P.M. warns of a hard shower starting in the morning.

To tell the weather when the weatherman is uncertain, consult your weather diary; weather has a habit of repeating itself after identical winds and other conditions. Even when the weatherman is correct, his predictions cannot apply to all areas; your locality will always have its peculiarities which only an old friend can recognize. Get friendly with your neighborhood weather—you'll find him good company. Look at the sky and tell the weather.

ABOUT THE AUTHOR

Eric Sloane was born in New York City and educated at Yale. Most of his life has been spent in New England, where he has combined a fascinating range of interests into a colorful and highly successful career, primarily as author-illustrator of more than twenty-four books on American history, arts, and artifacts.

A lifelong interest in the lore and science of weather brought him to a long association with weather forecasting and aviation—he has been a pilot and was the first television weatherman.

Perhaps the most important task he has undertaken is to show, through his landscape and cloud paintings, his collections of American furniture, artifacts, and Americana, his meticulous restoration of more than twenty houses and buildings in the Colonial style (including his present studio and home in Cornwall Bridge, Connecticut), and his many books, the concrete form and reality of the early American experience and the lives of its citizens.

His paintings are exhibited regularly in New York galleries, and his restoration projects include the Sloane-Stanley Museum, specializing in American tools and artifacts, located in Kent Furnace, Connecticut. He is a member of the National Academy and a recipient of the Valley Forge Freedoms Foundation Leadership Award.